sumoji

Published by SevenOaks
An imprint of Carlton Books Ltd
20 Mortimer Street
London W1T 3JW

Copyright © 2018 Carlton Books Ltd
Emoji artwork supplied by Emoji One (http://emojione.com)

A CIP catalogue for this book is available from the British Library.

ISBN 978-1-78177-868-5

Printed in China

10 9 8 7 6 5 4 3 2 1

sumoji

MORE THAN 💯 EMOJI SUDOKU

SEVENOAKS

Contents

Welcome to *Sumoji*!

What is 'Sumoji'? Simply, it's Sudoku... with Emojis! A fun and innovative new combination of two of Japan's greatest exports.

Sudoku took the Western puzzle world by storm years ago, and has showed no signs of stopping its domination of puzzle books any time soon. It's a solid puzzle favourite that draws people in with its simplicity – a newbie can learn how to solve them in minutes – but is so addictive it keeps them coming back time and time again. Every Sudoku puzzle is different, but looking at all those numbers can be repetitive... so we've livened it up with everyone's favorite 😍, 🥒 and, of course, 💩!

Emojis are the fastest-growing – and most fun – language in the world! Ninety-two percent of people online now use Emojis on a daily basis, and young people everywhere delight in baffling their older, supposedly wiser, relatives with them. In music videos, TV shows, and even a Hollywood appearance in *The Emoji Movie*, they are now inescapable. Even the esteemed Oxford Dictionary has been forced to recognize Emojis: 😆 was recently named their Word of the Year.

With *Sumoji*, Emojis will now break down the final barrier and become accepted as a replacement for numbers too. So break out your 🤔 and use 😍, 🎨 and 😋 and a whole host of other cheerful and vibrant Emojis to work your way through a variety of Easy, Medium and Hard puzzles. Using the supplied colorful stickers to fill in the missing Emojis, 😳 your way through all three chapters and see how close you can get to *100*.

Sumoji

Sumoji is solved in exactly the same way as a regular Sudoku – it just involves having more fun!

Each row, column, and 3x3 grid should contain one of each of the nine Emojis listed at the top of the page. If any appear twice then you've made a mistake.

Good luck!

1

Easy

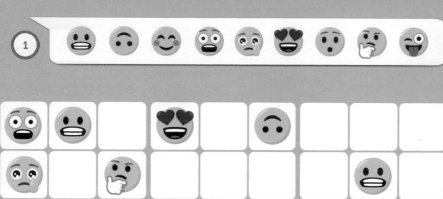

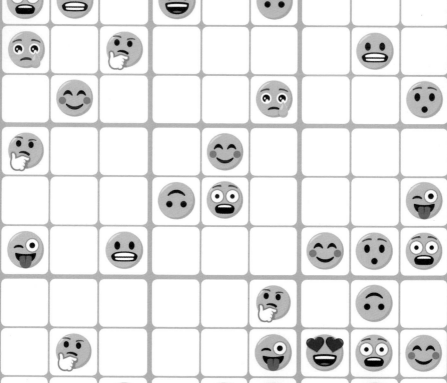

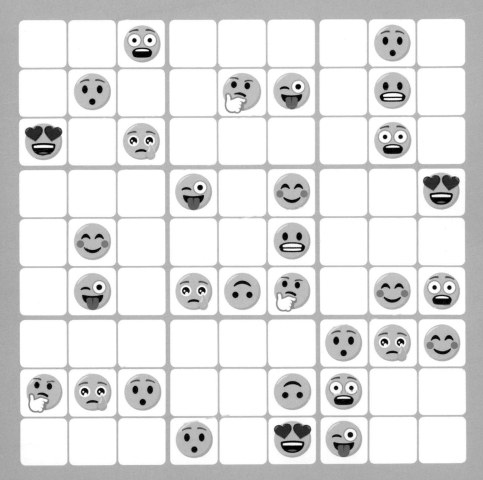

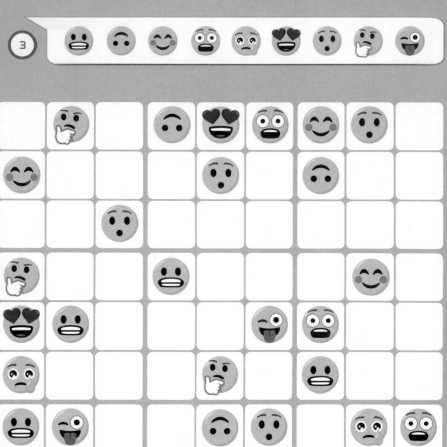

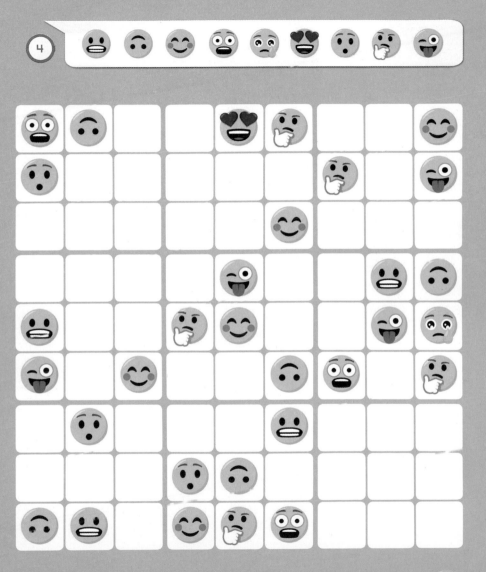

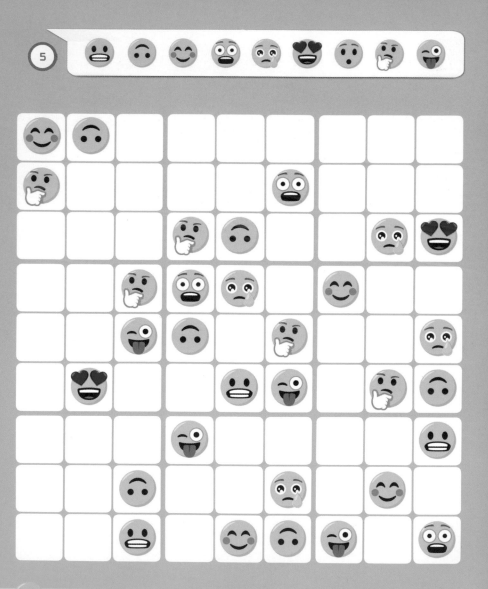

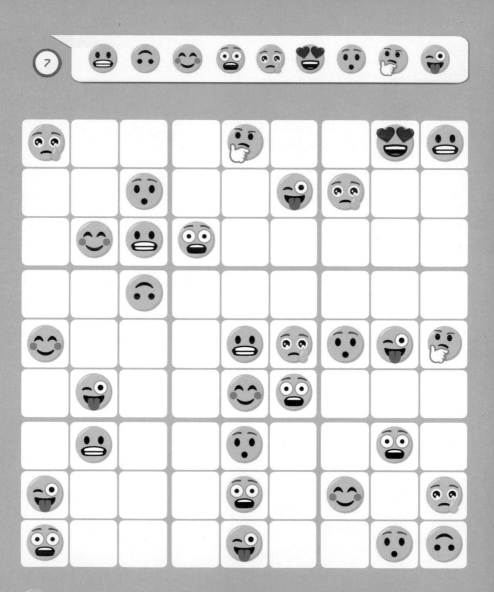

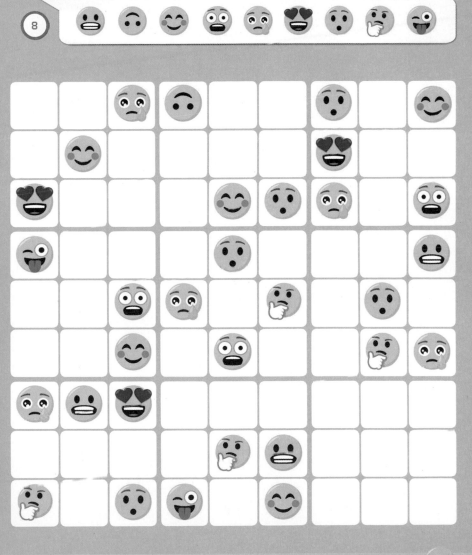

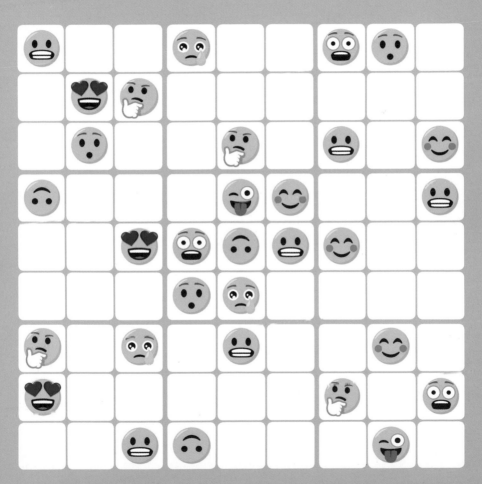

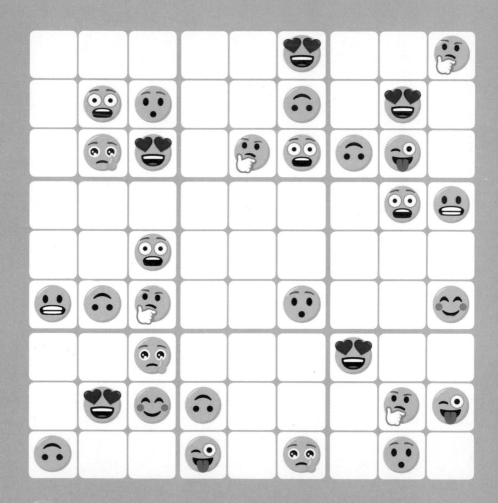

120

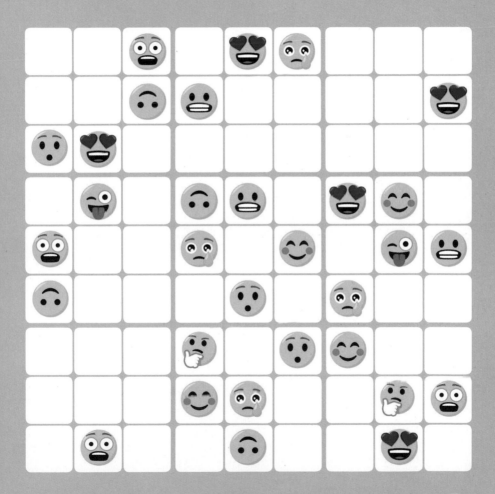

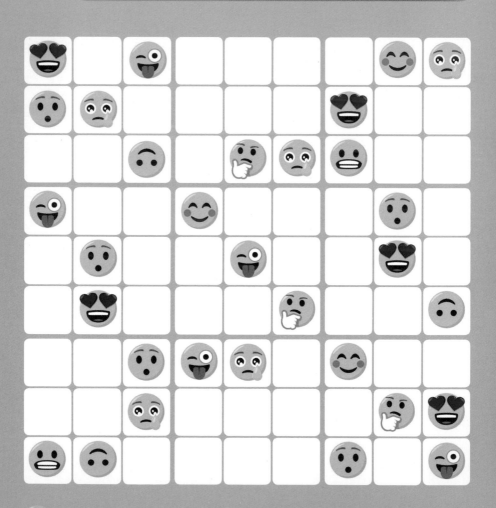

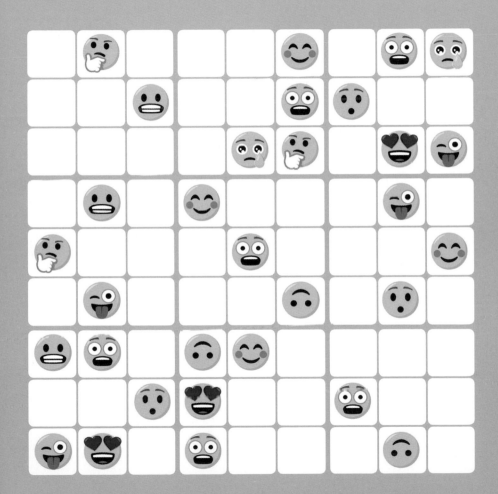

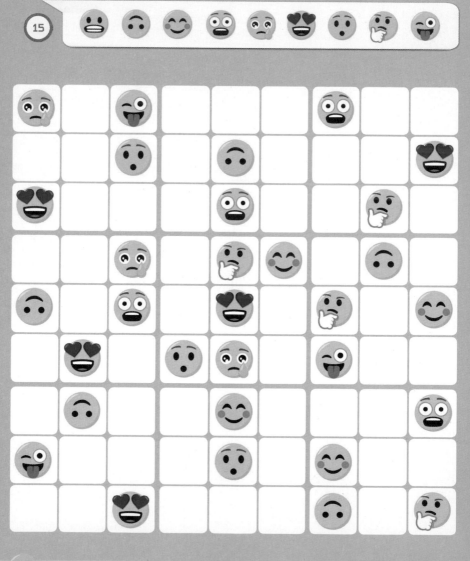

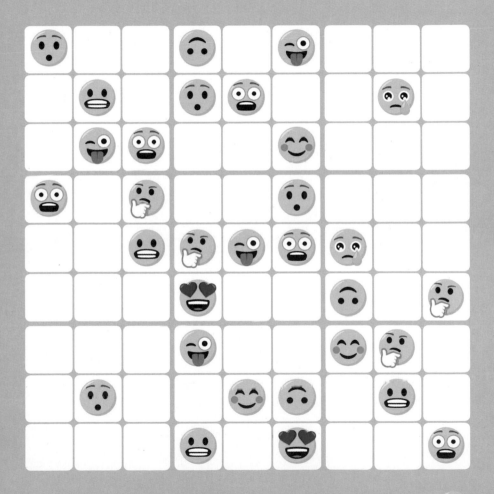

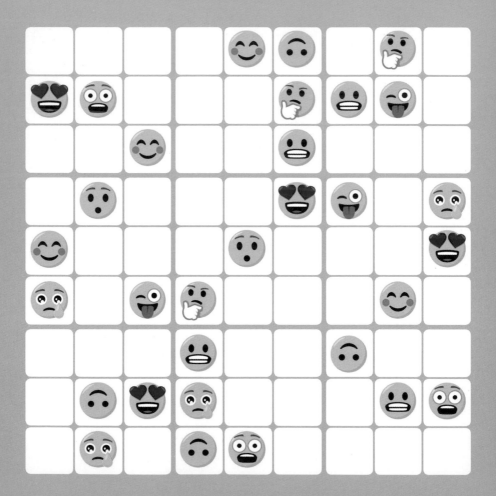

  122

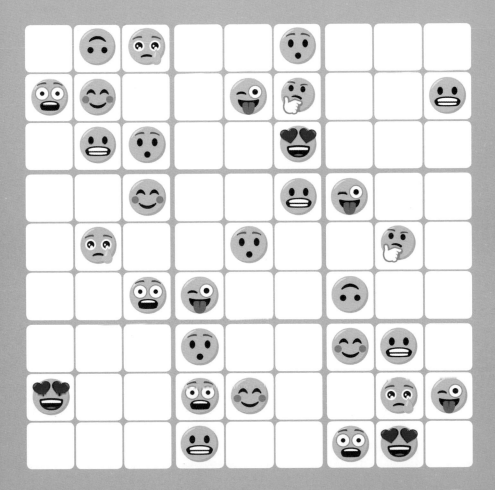

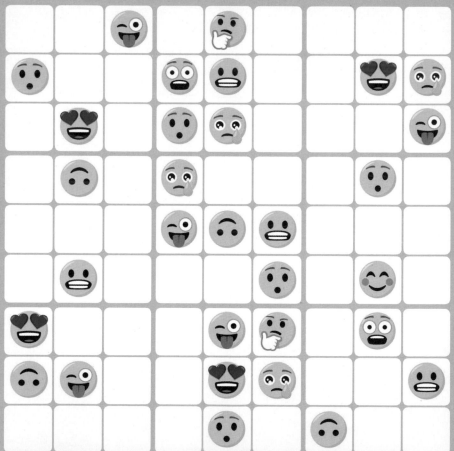

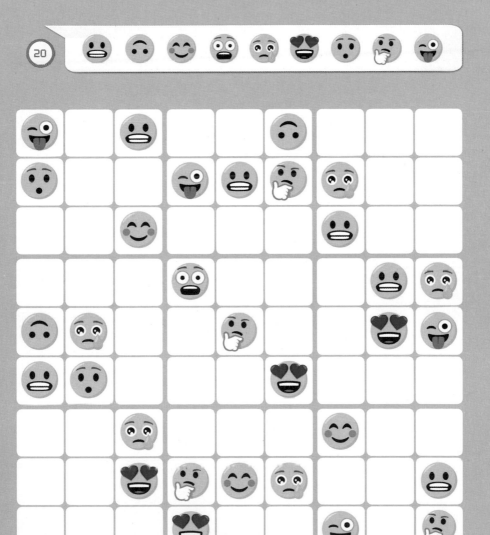

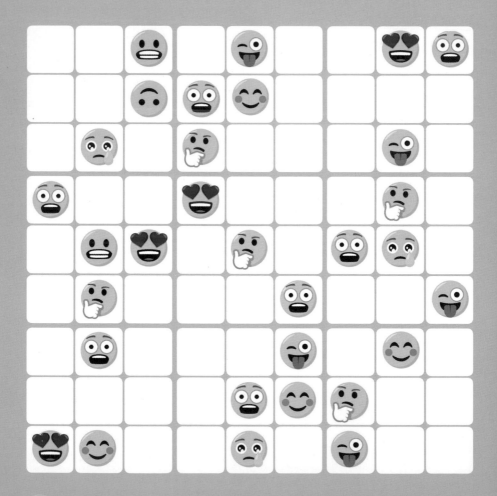

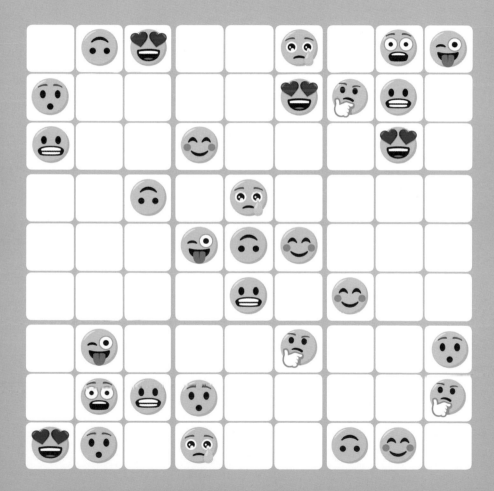

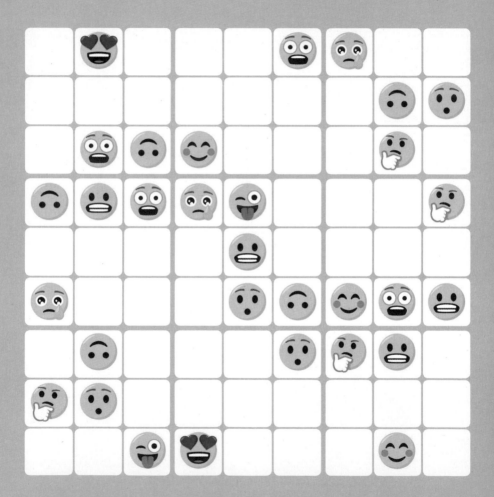

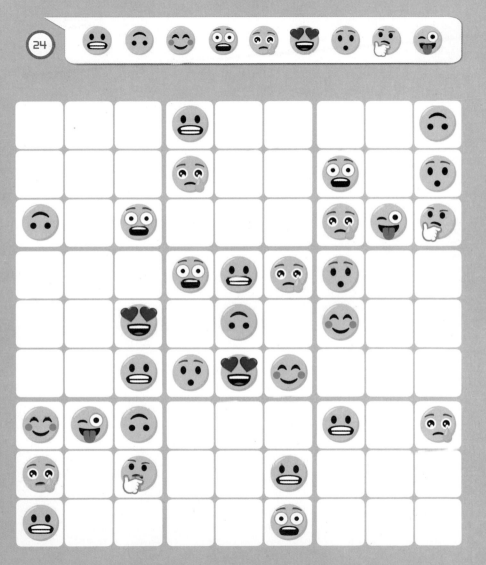

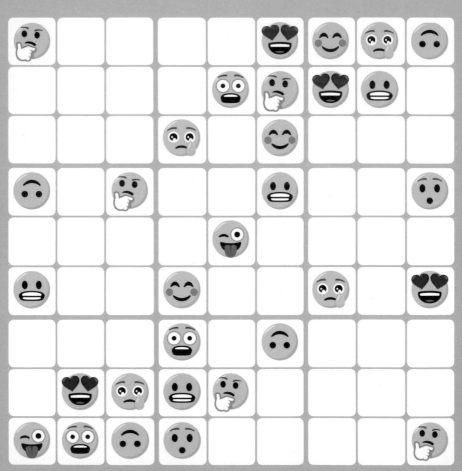

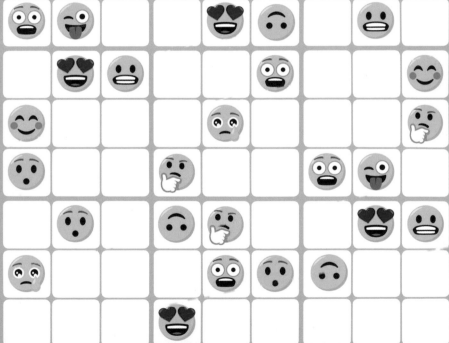

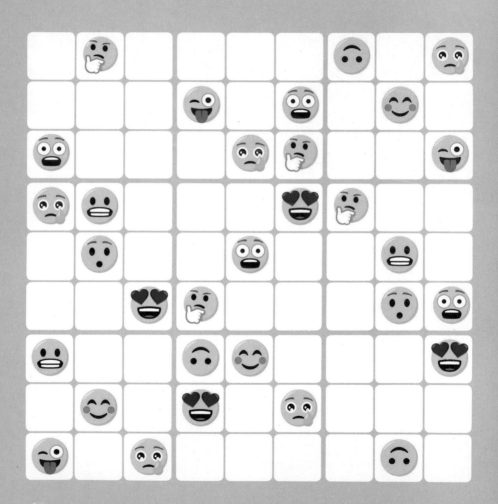

124

EASY SUMOJI

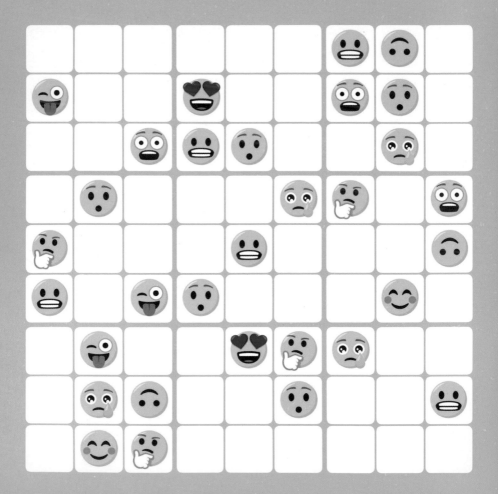

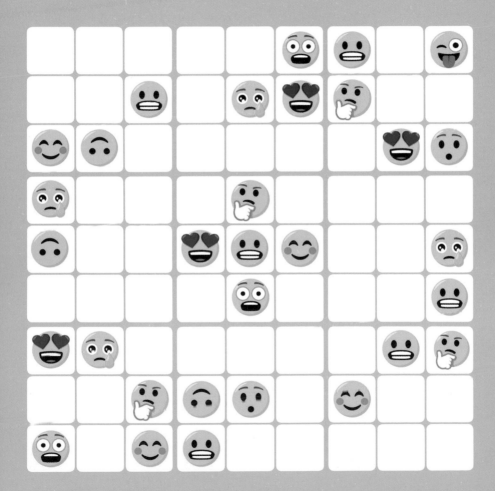

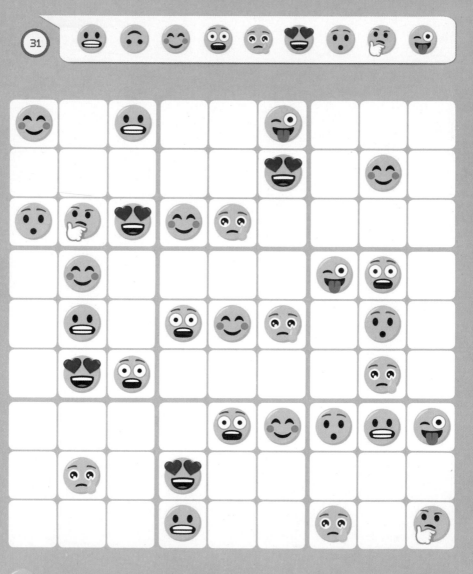

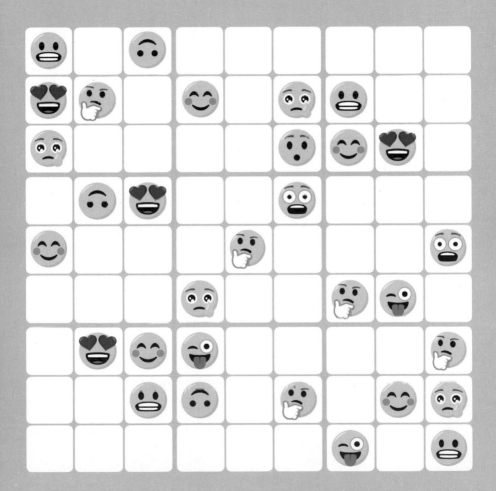

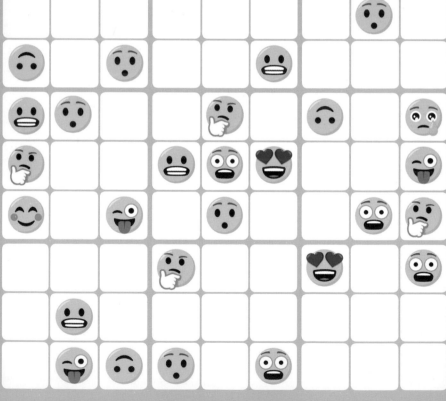

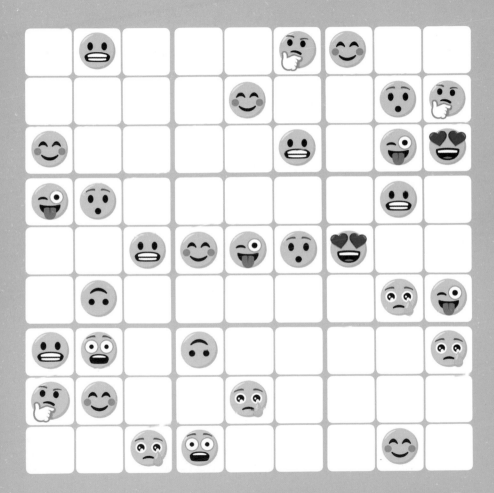

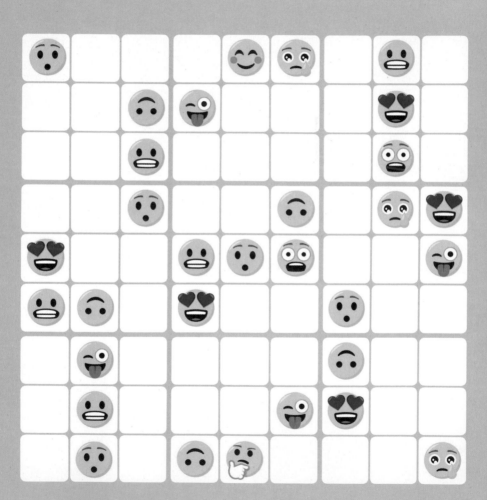

Medium

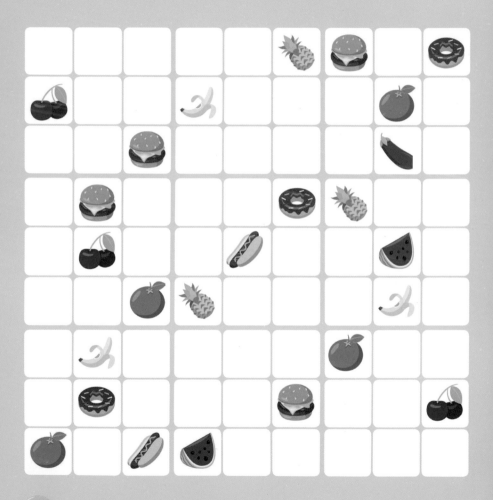

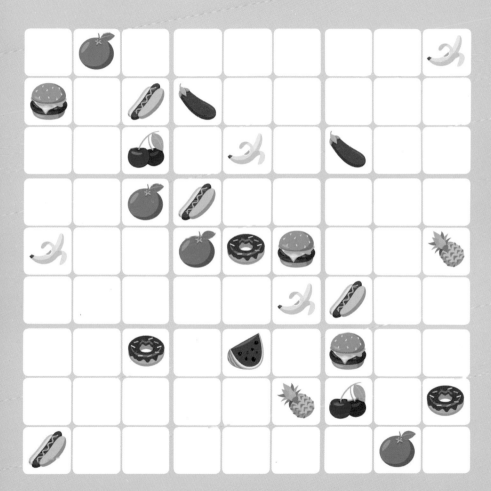

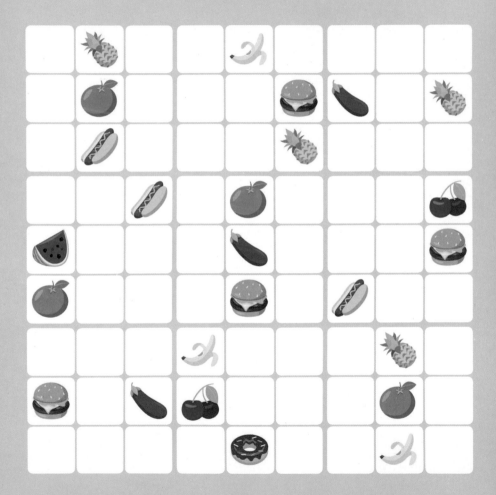

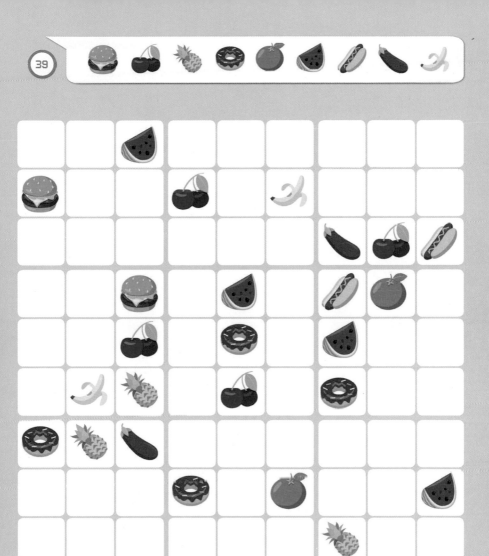

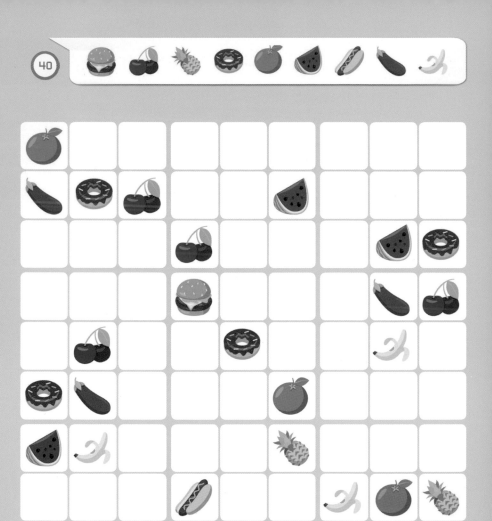

 128

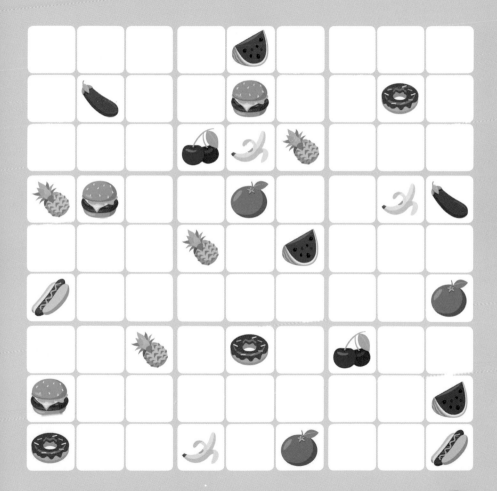

MEDIUM SUMOJI 51

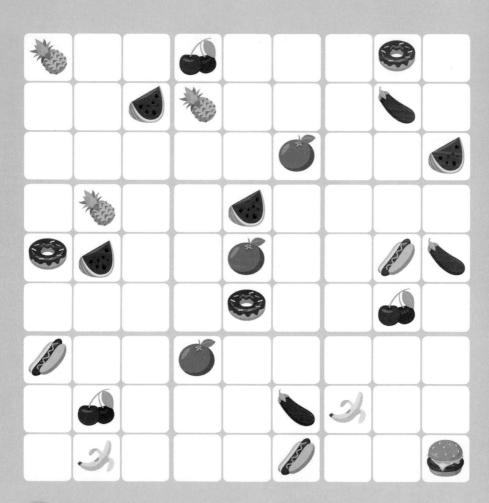

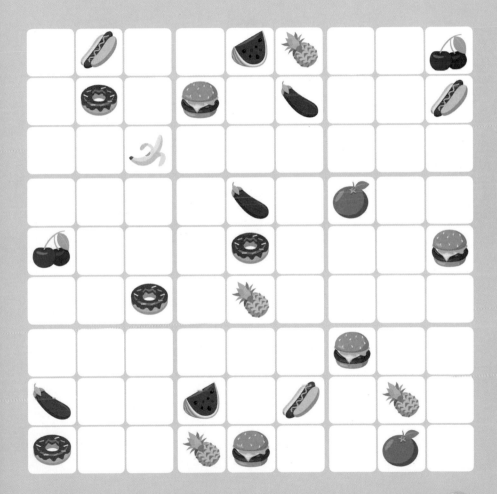

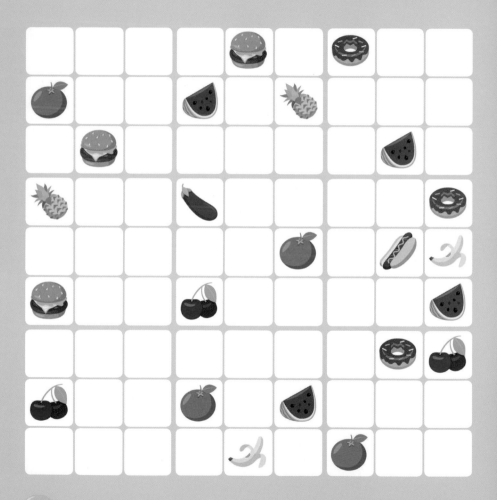

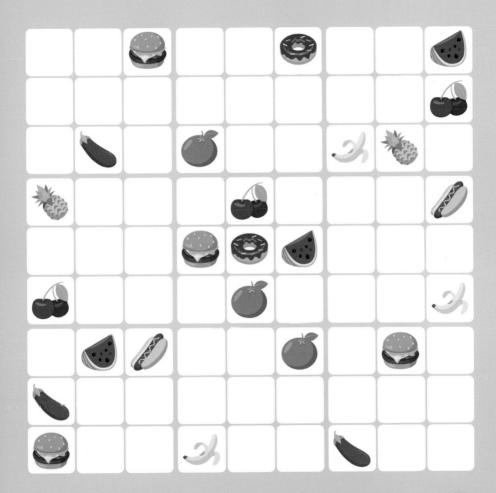

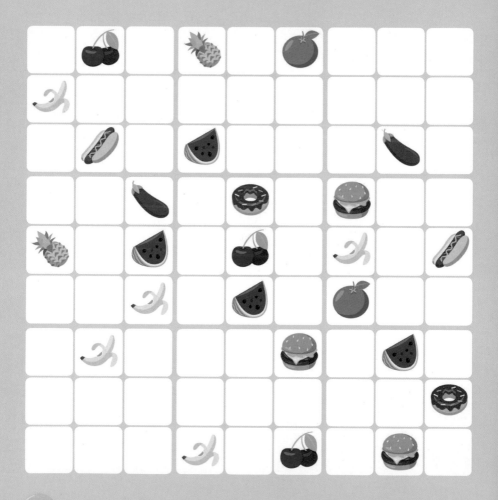

 129

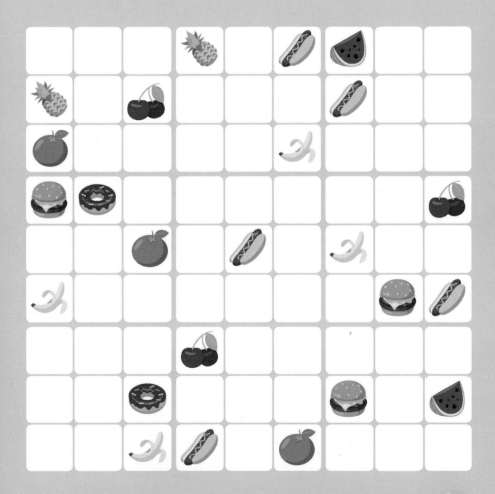

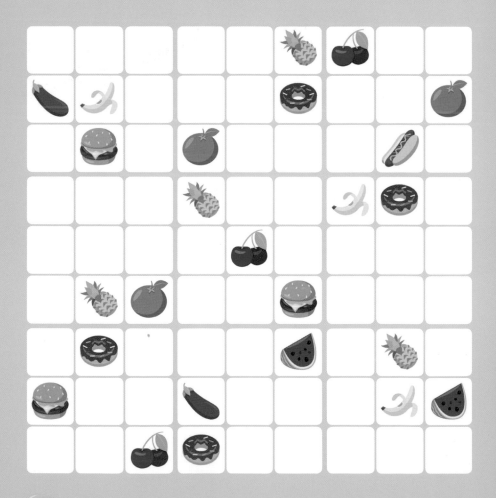

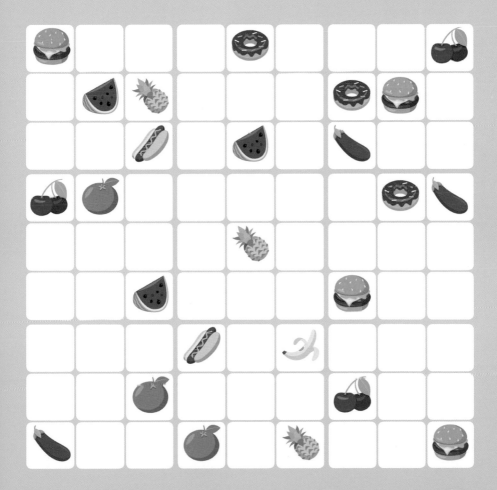

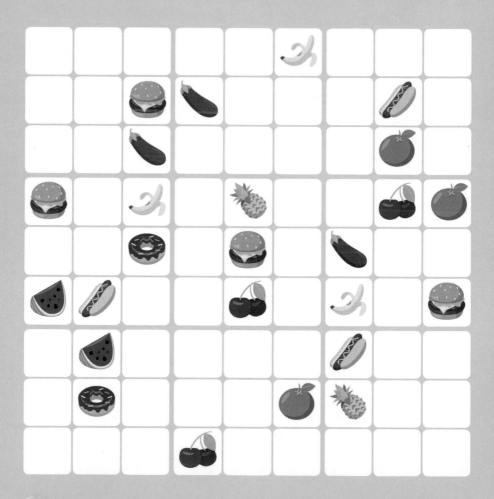

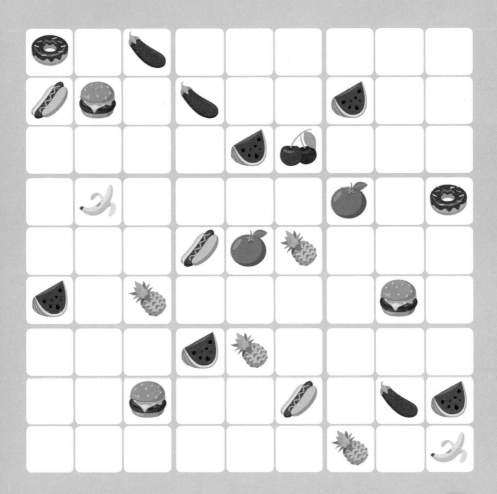

MEDIUM SUMOJI 61

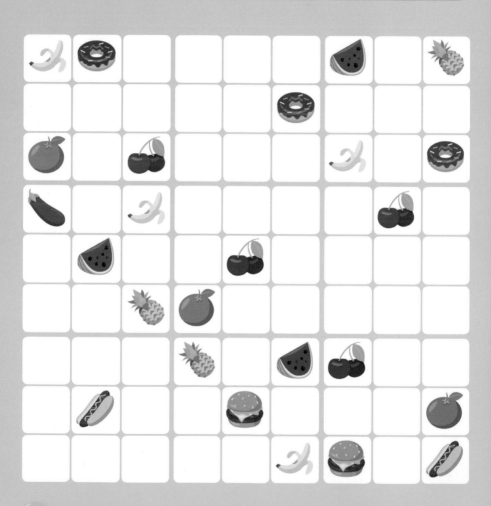

131

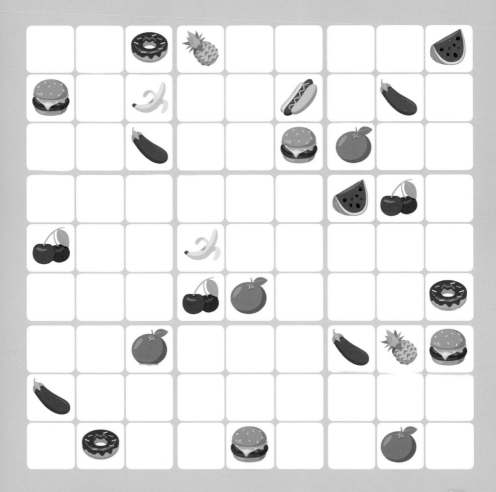

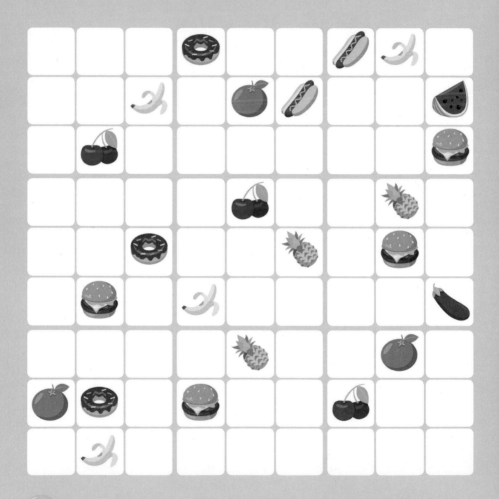

131

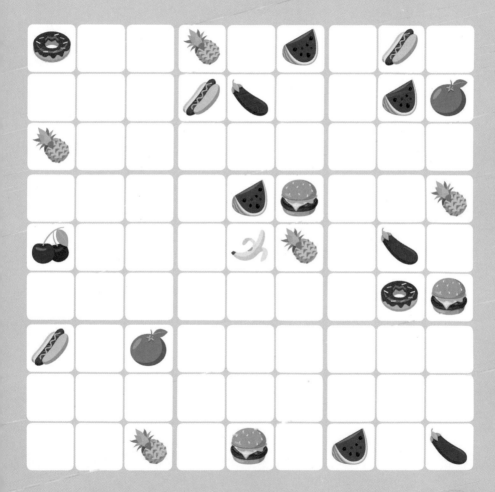

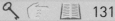 131

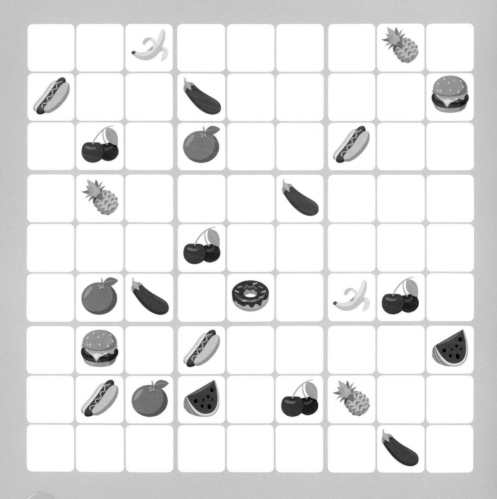

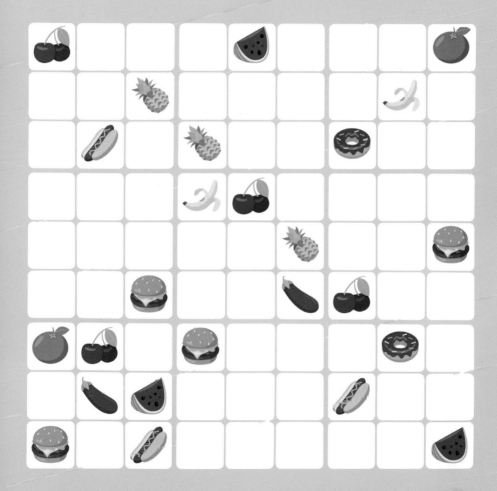

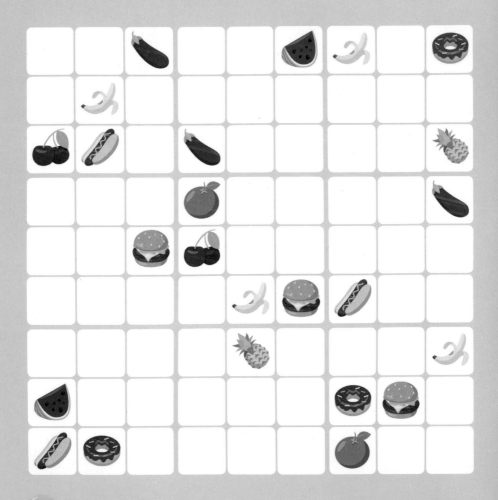

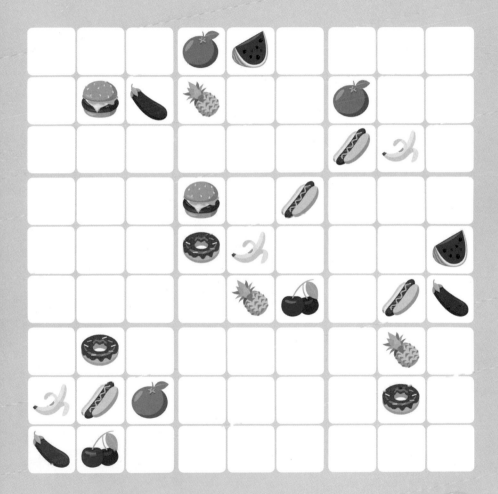

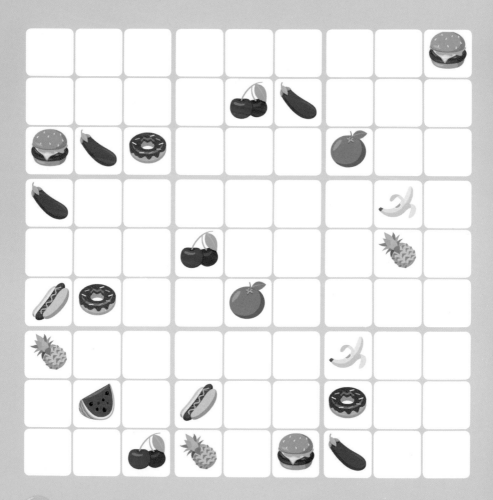

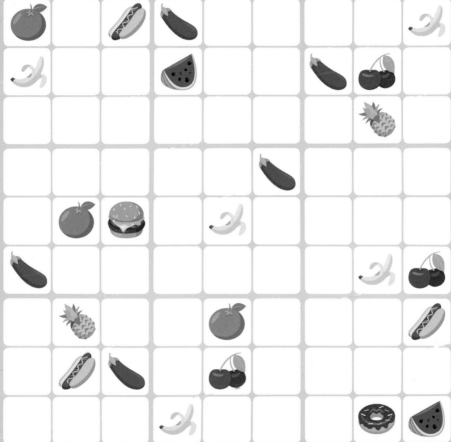

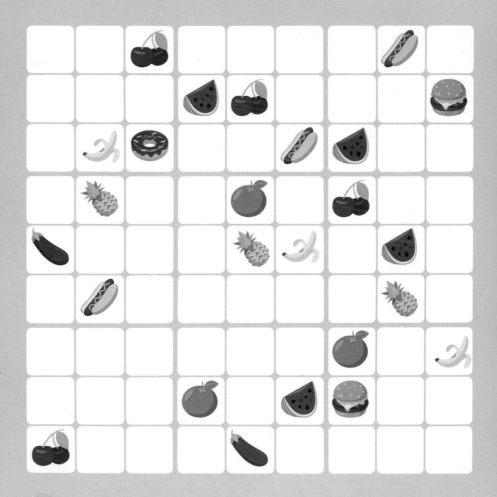

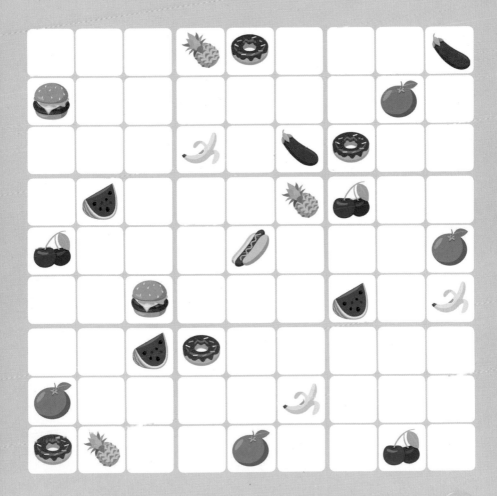

MEDIUM SUMOJI 73

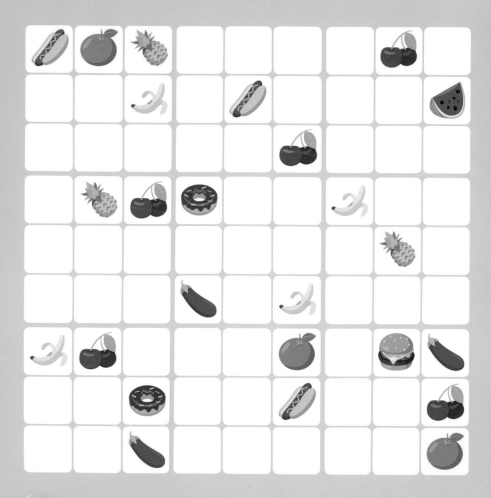

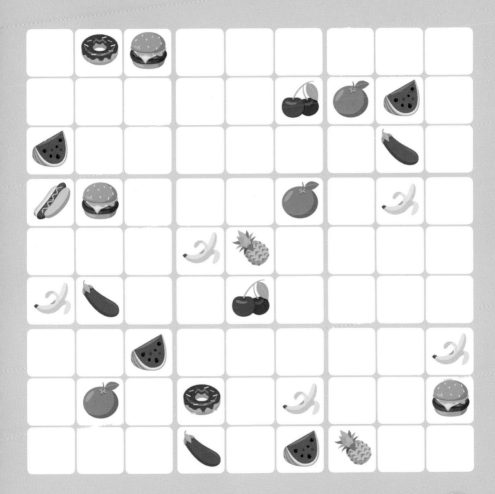

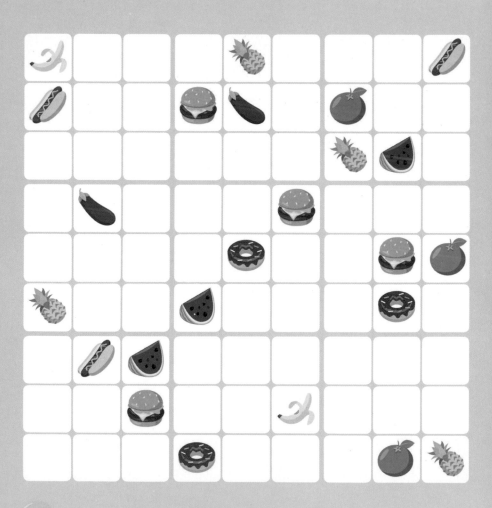

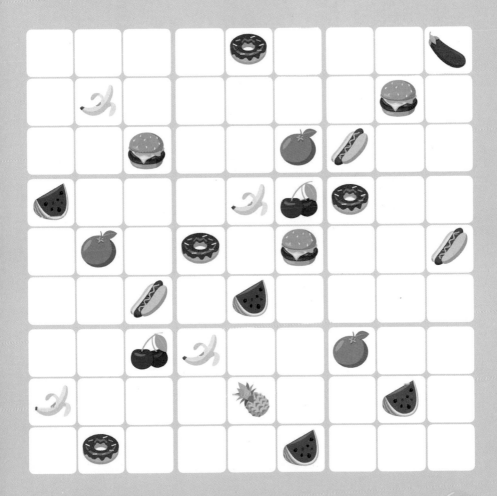

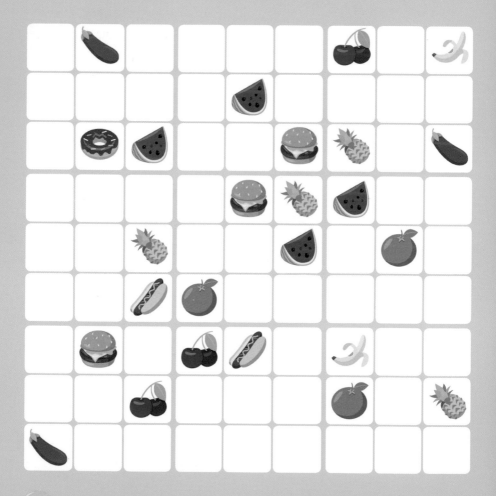

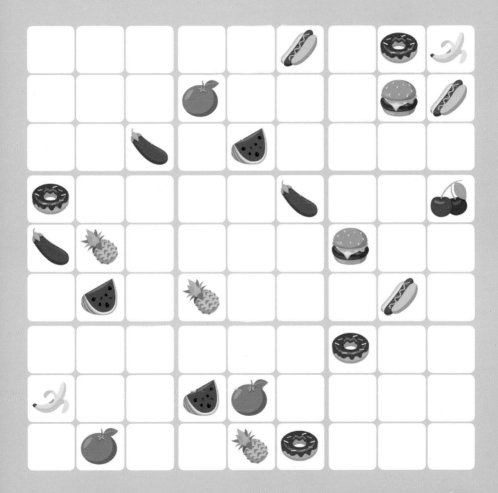

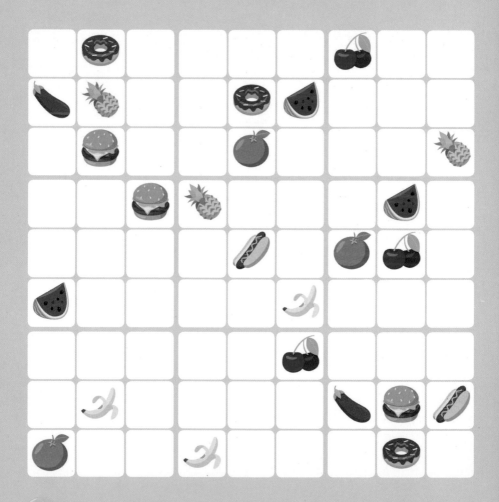

3

Hard

 137

 HARD SUMOJI 89

HARD SUMOJI 93

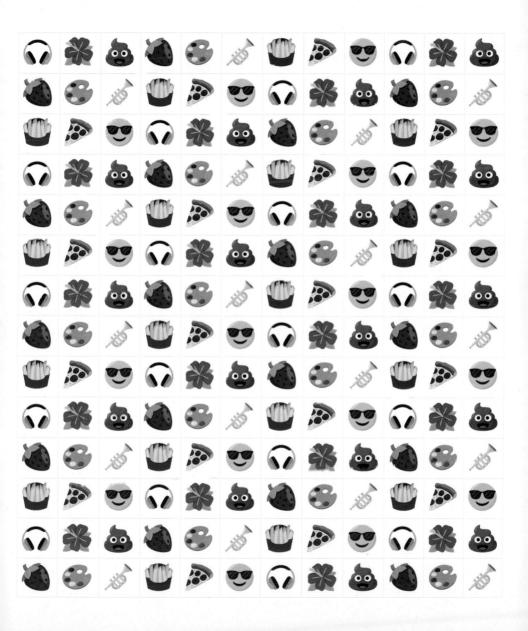

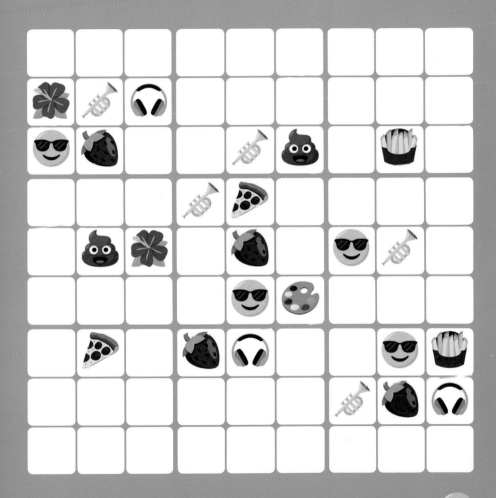

 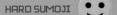

   140

 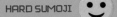

 141

142

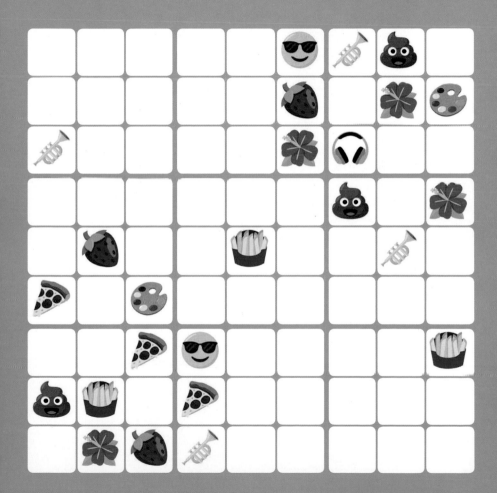

 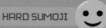

4

Solutions

1

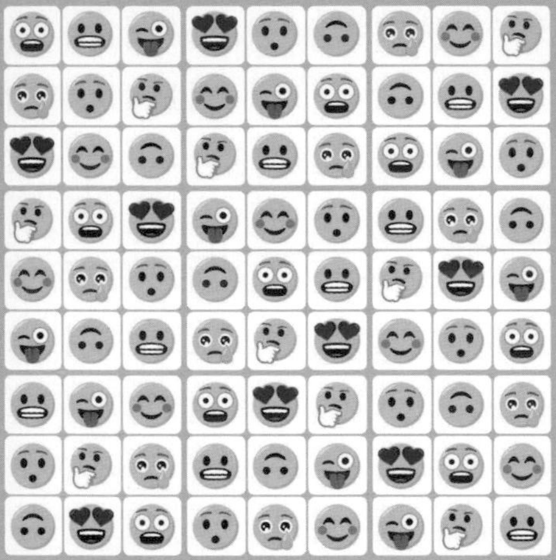

2

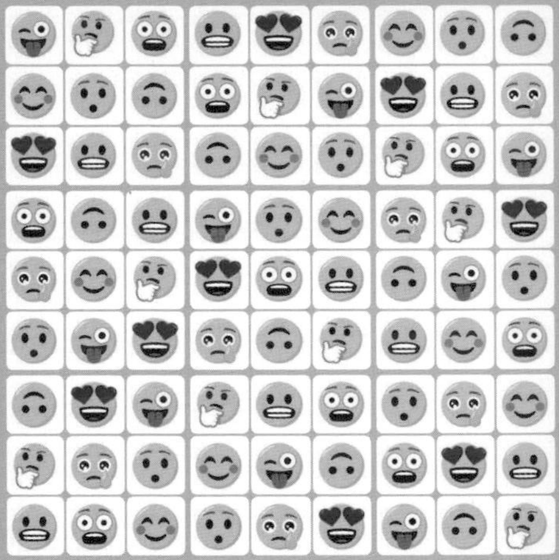

3

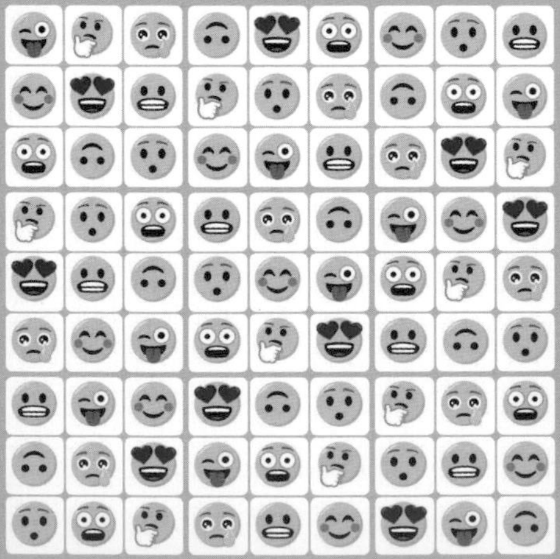

4

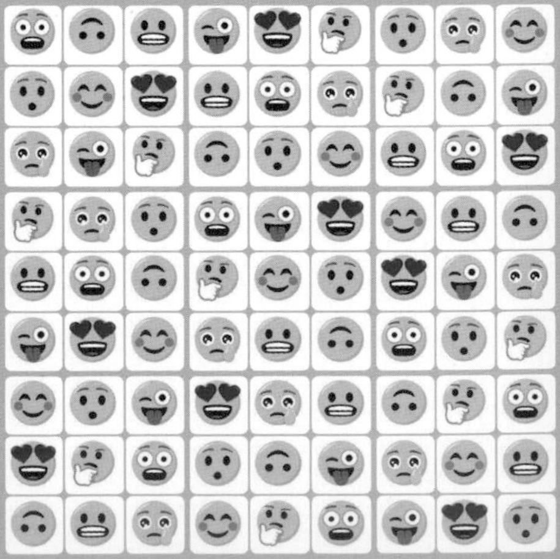

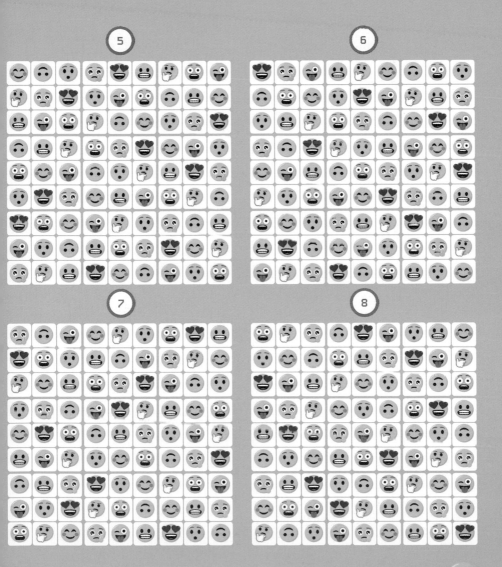

9

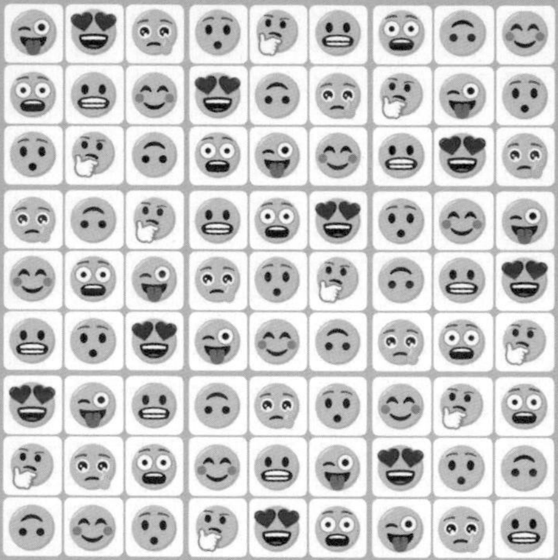

10

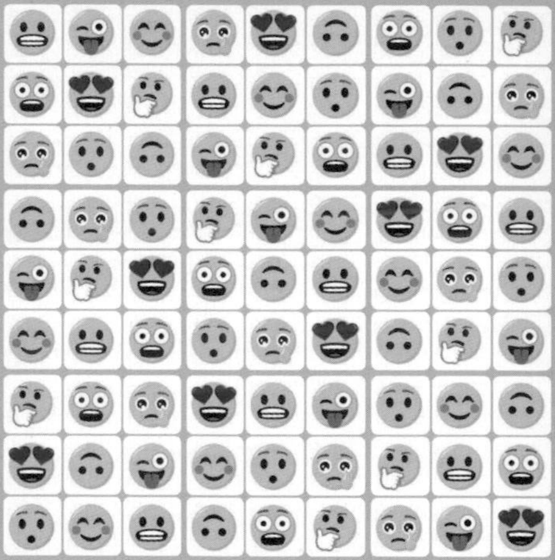

11

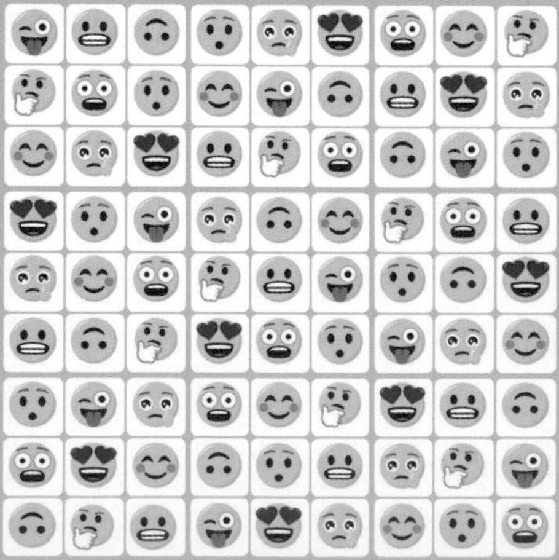

12

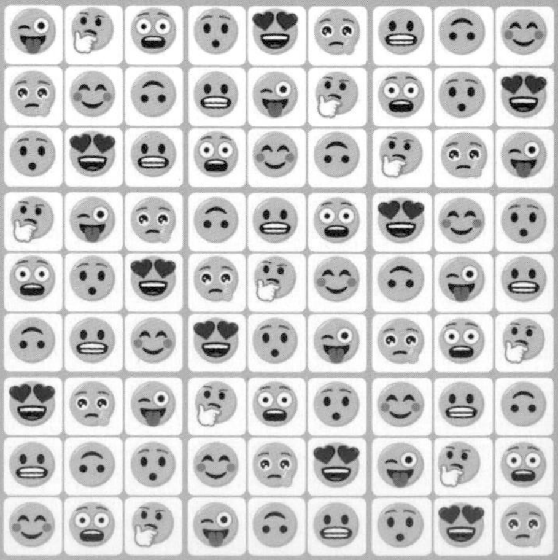

13

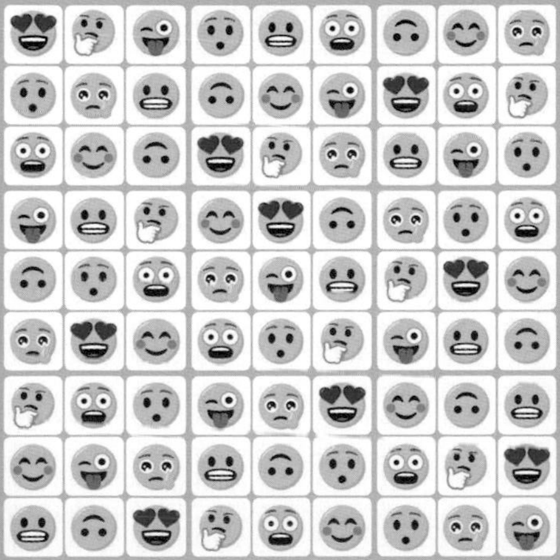

14

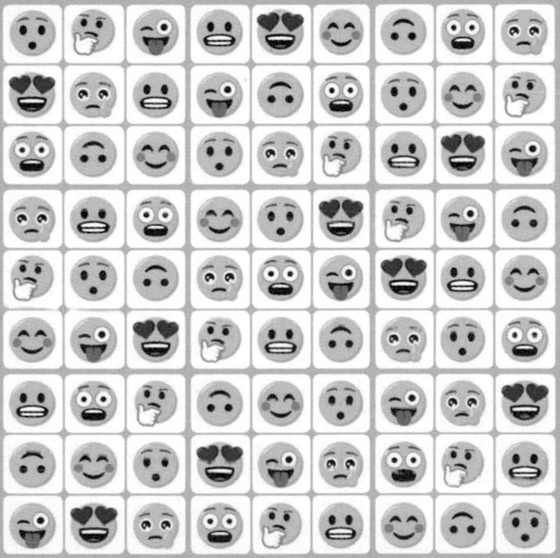

15

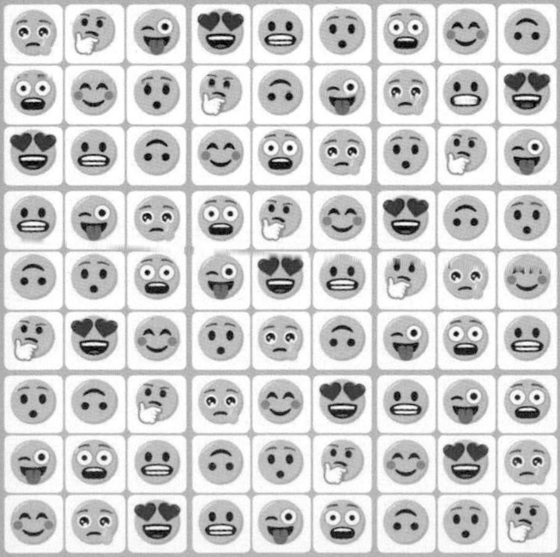

16

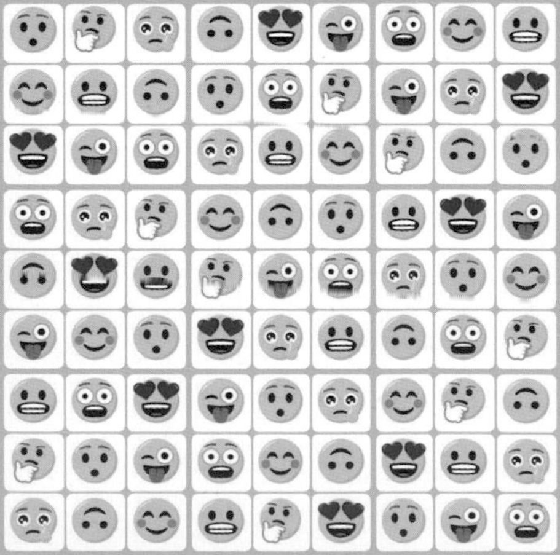

17

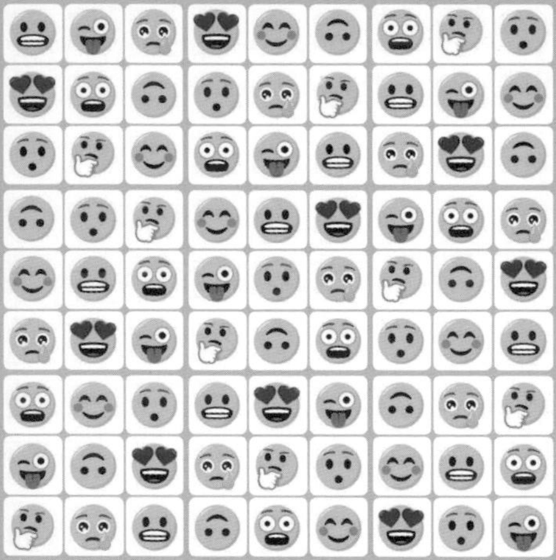

18

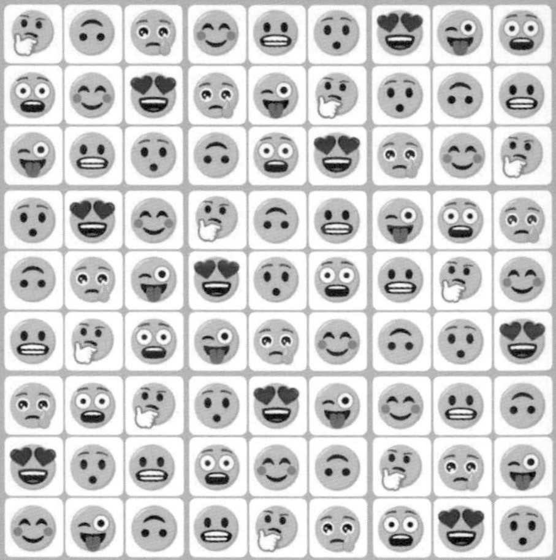

19

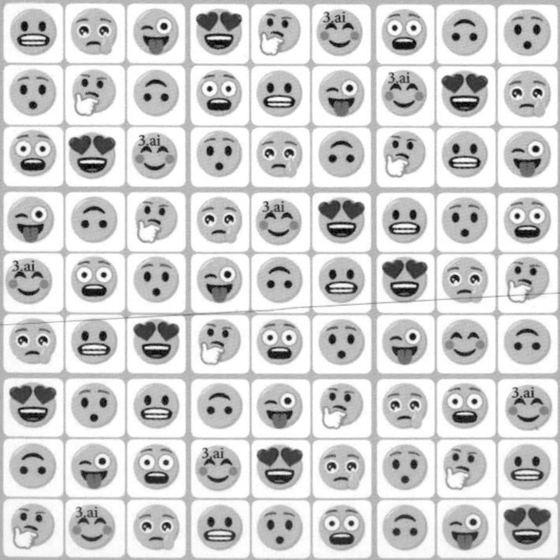

20

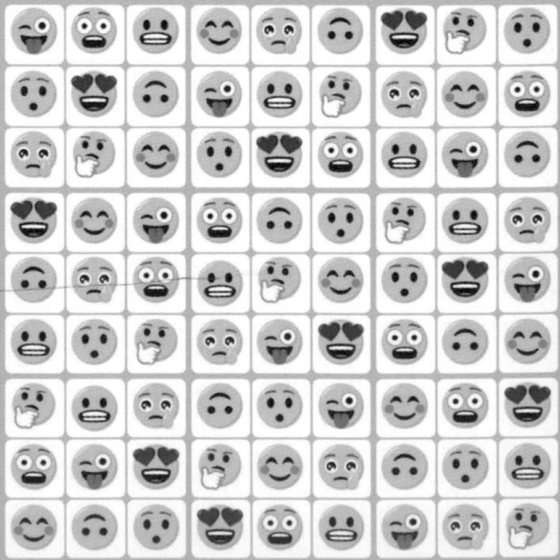

21

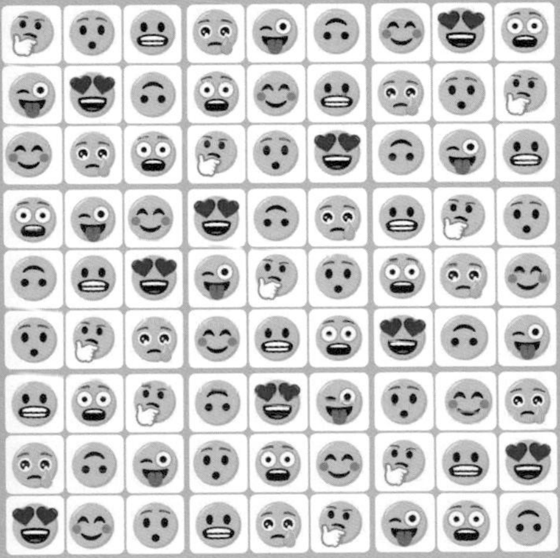

22

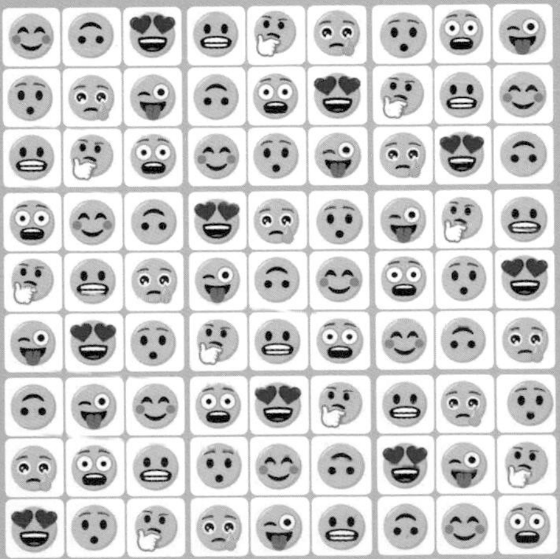

23

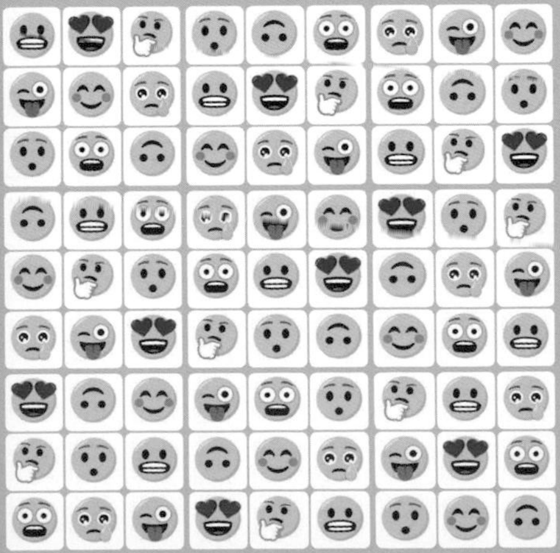

24

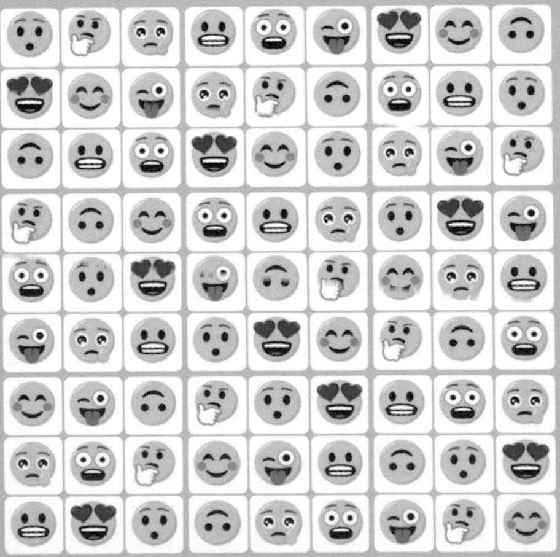

25

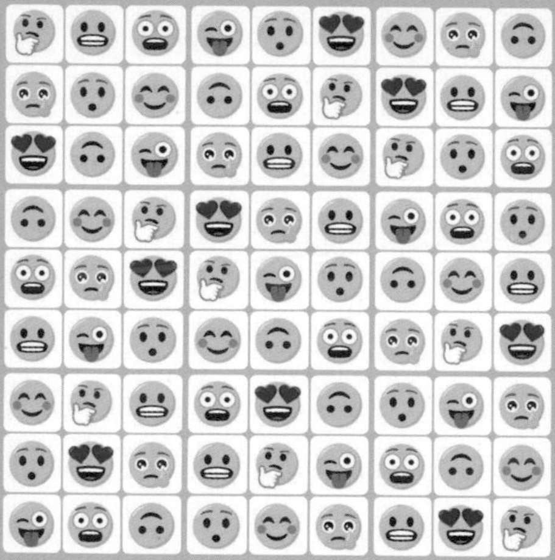

26

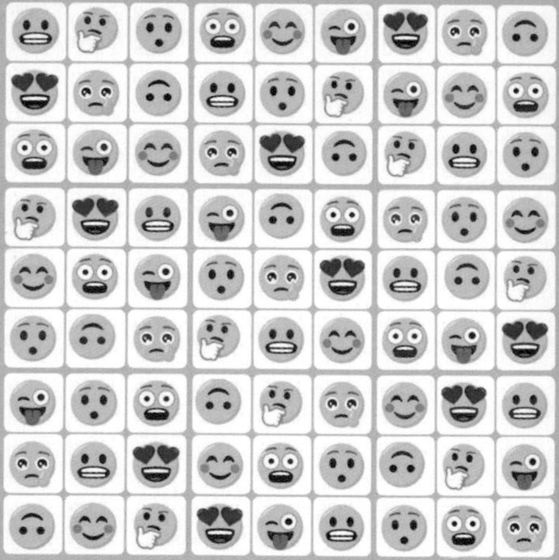

27

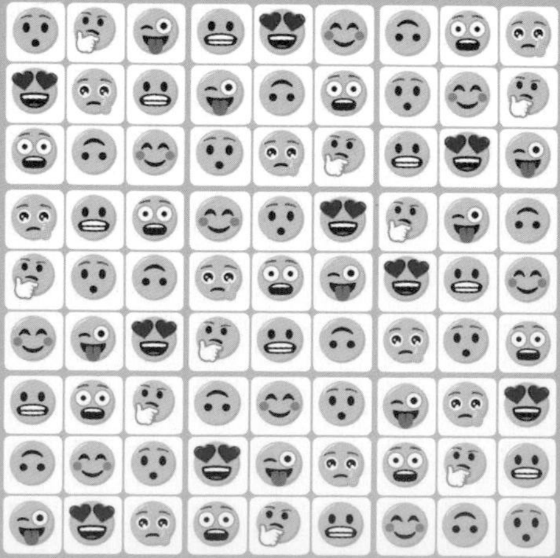

28

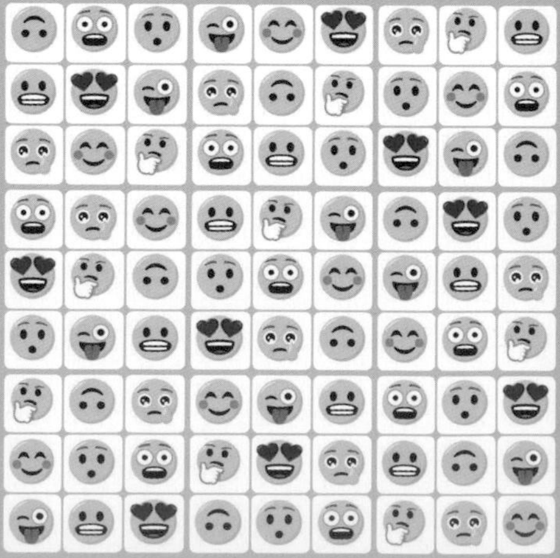

29

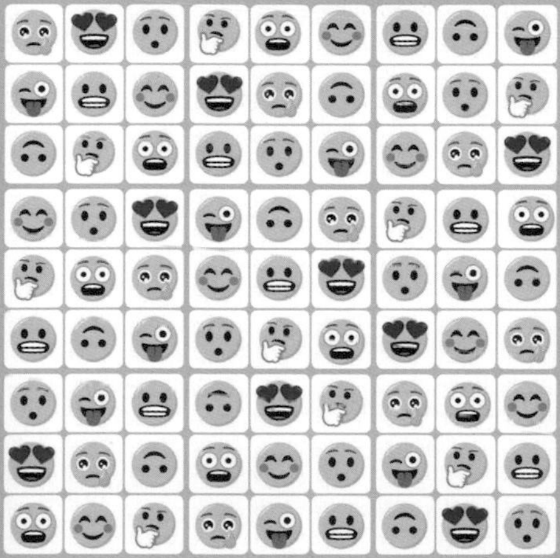

30

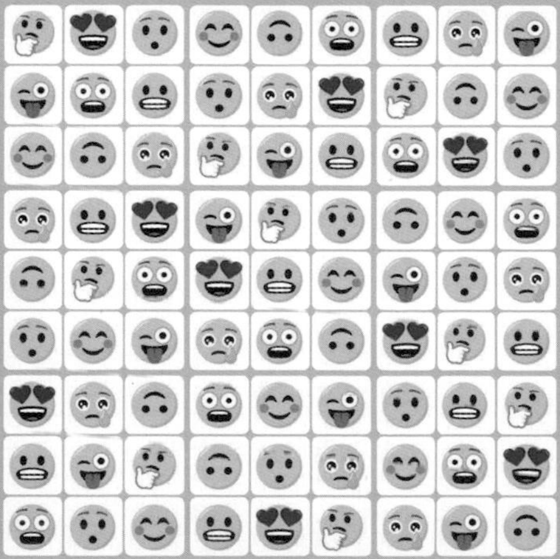

31

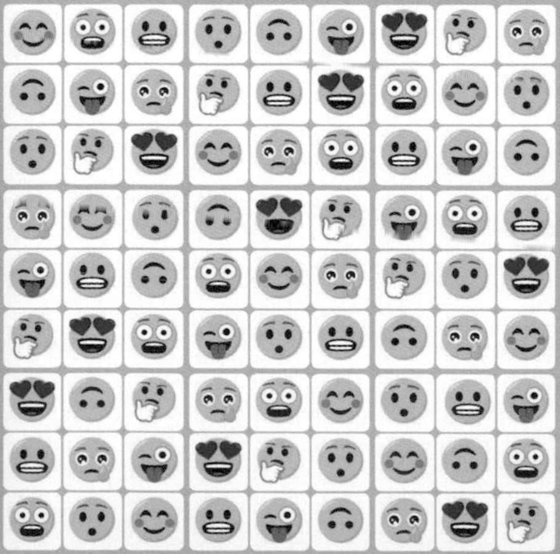

32

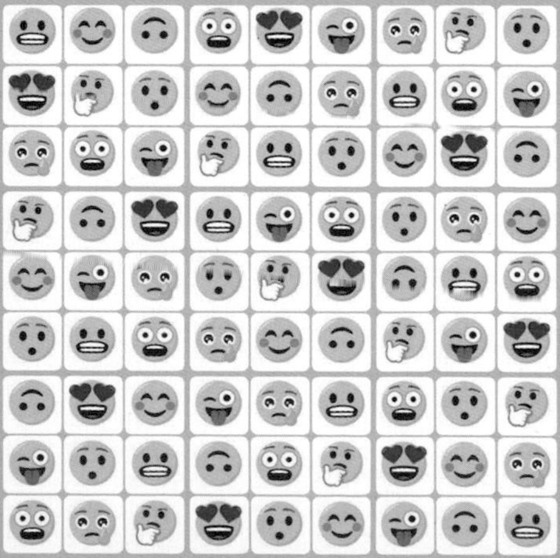

33

34

35

SOLUTIONS: EASY

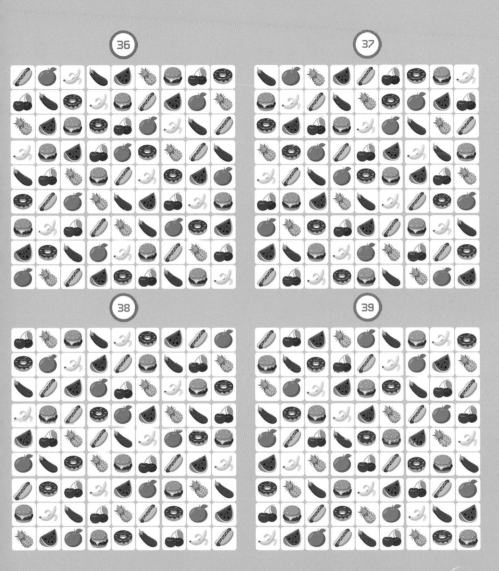

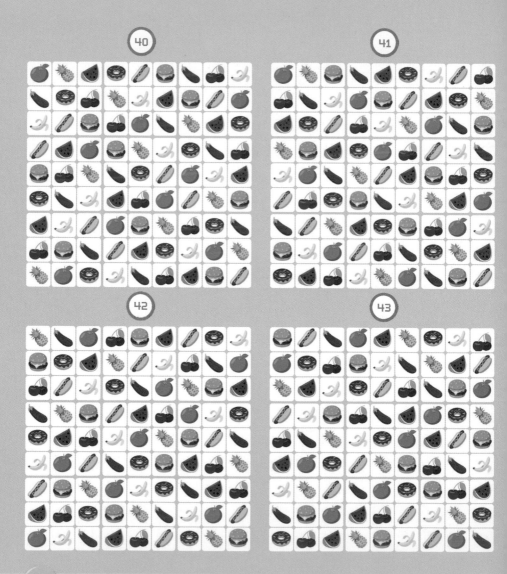

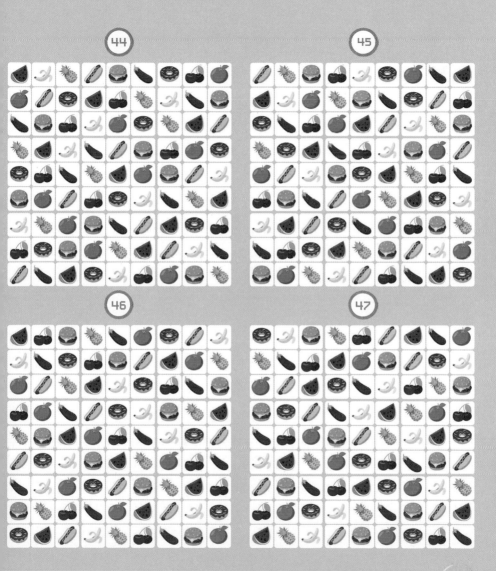

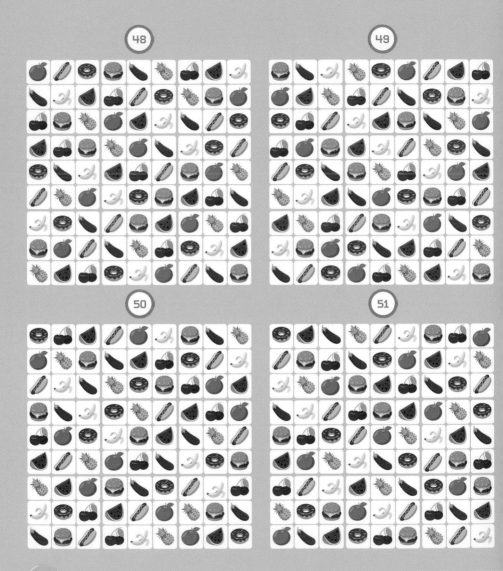

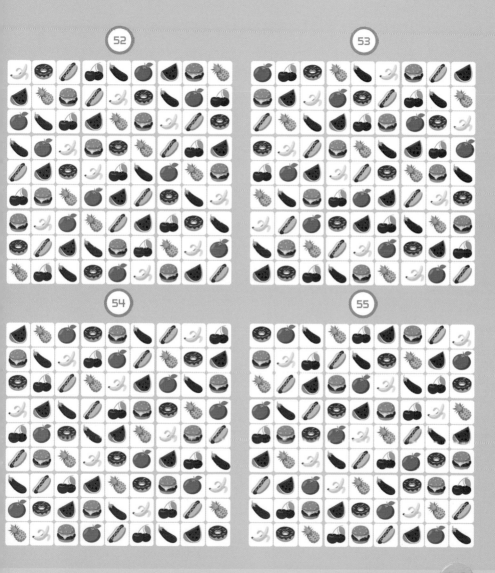

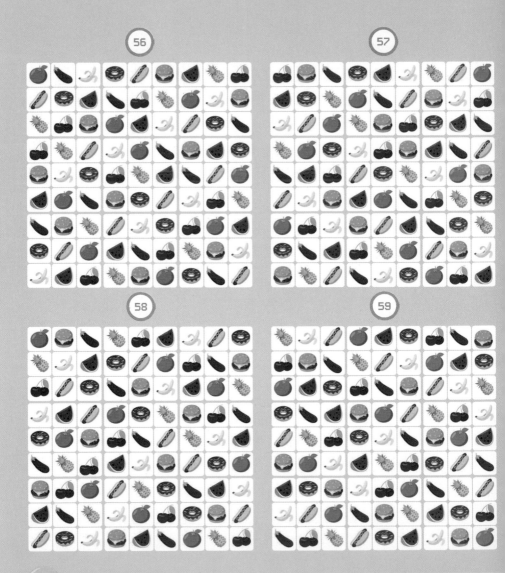

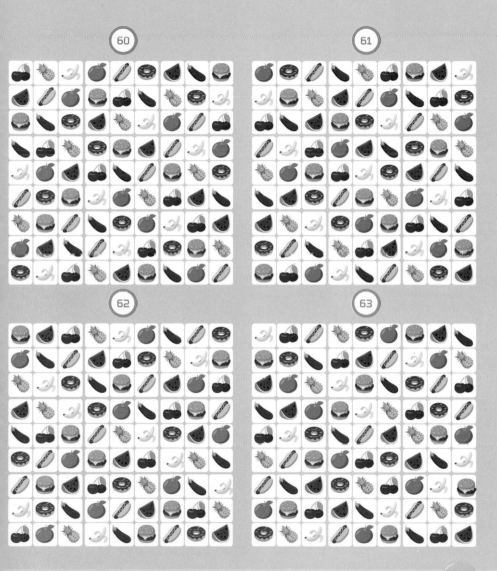

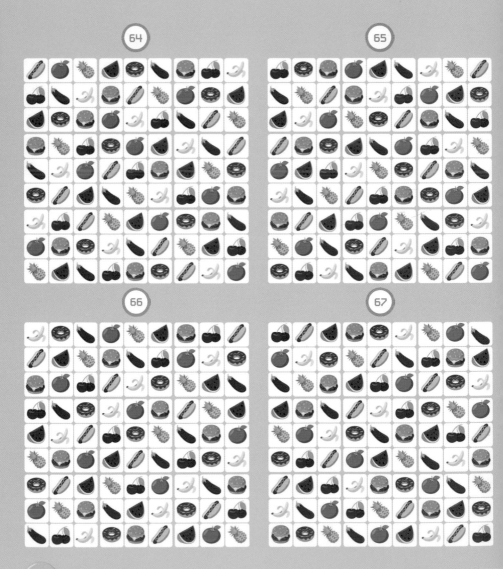

SOLUTIONS: MEDIUM

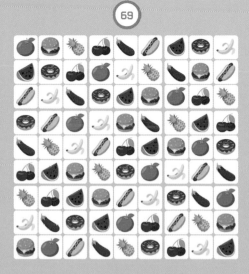

68

69

70

SOLUTIONS: HARD

75

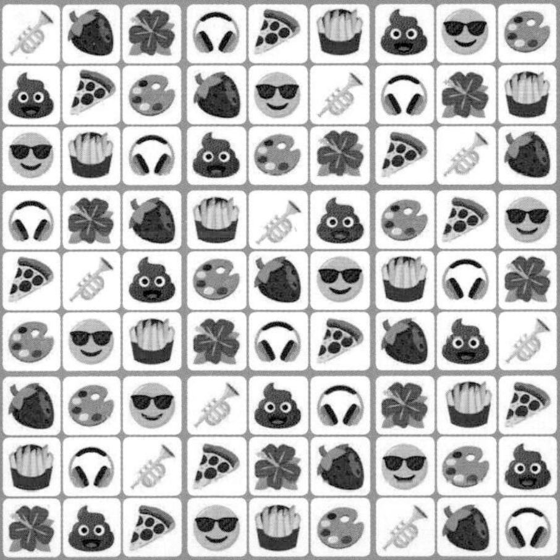

76

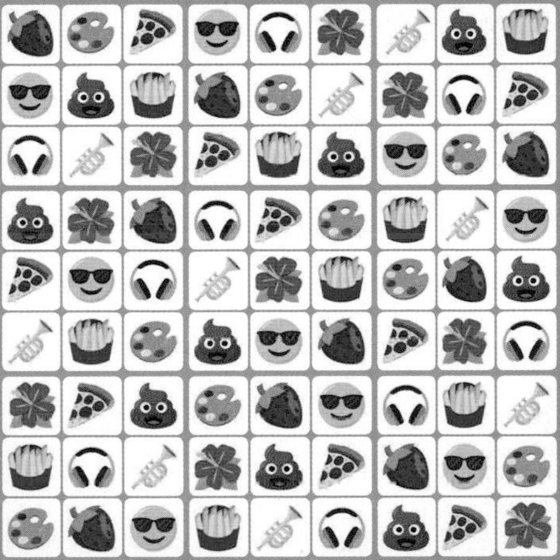

77

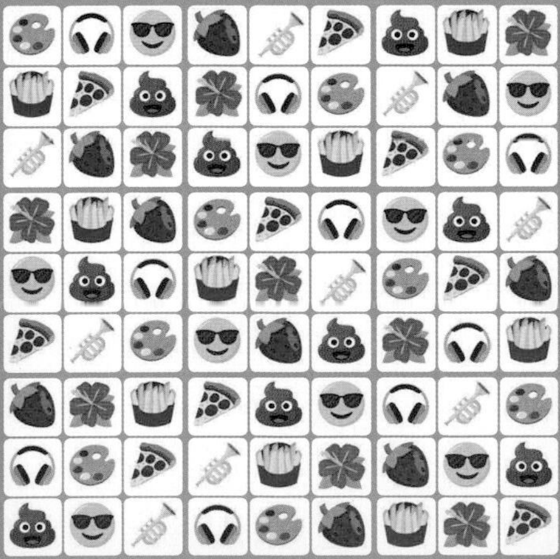

78

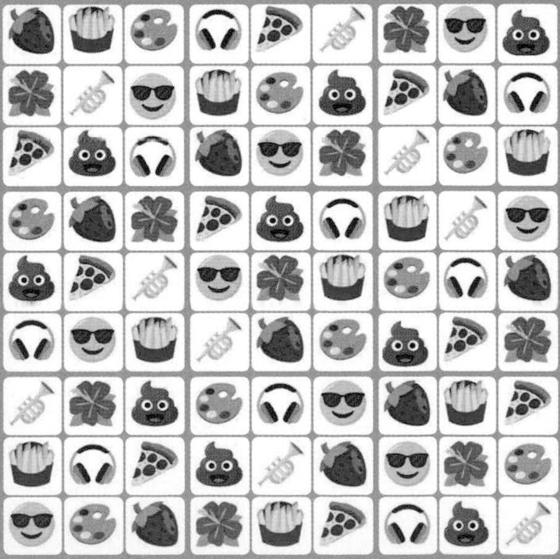

79

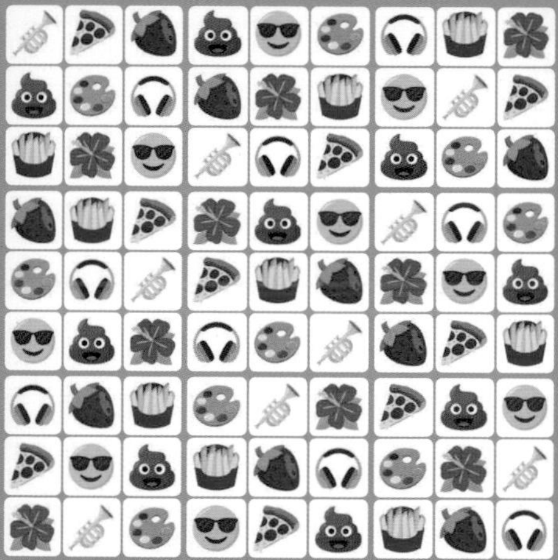

80

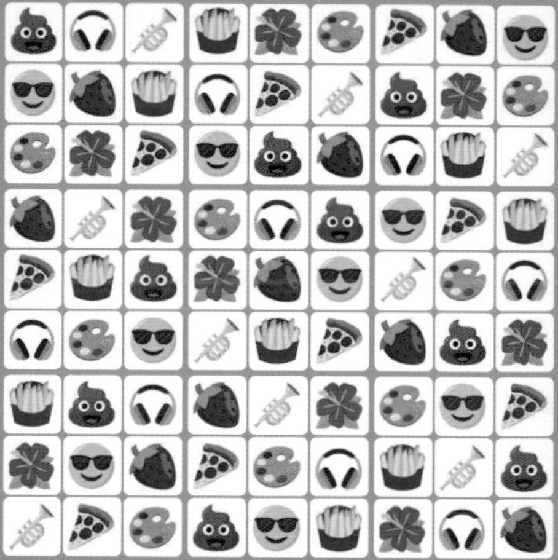

81

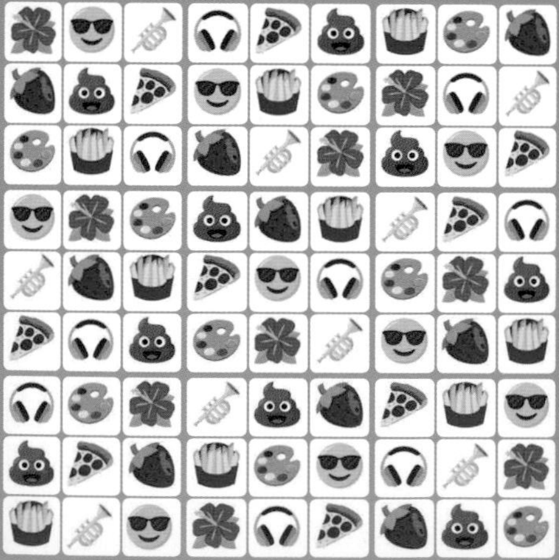

82

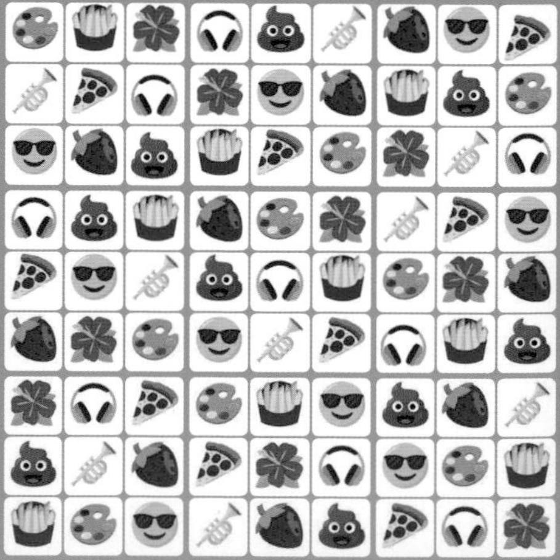

83

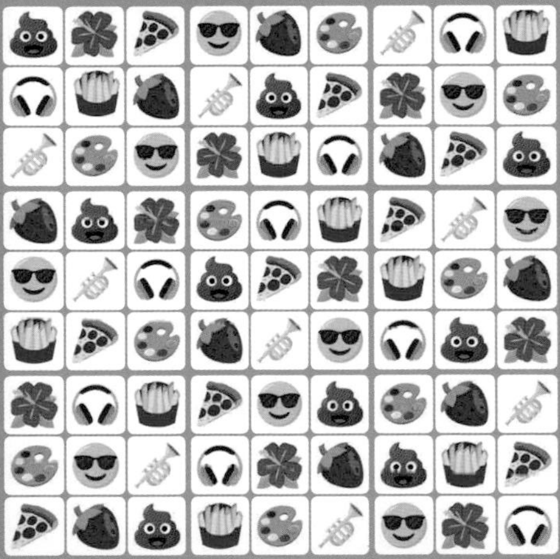

84

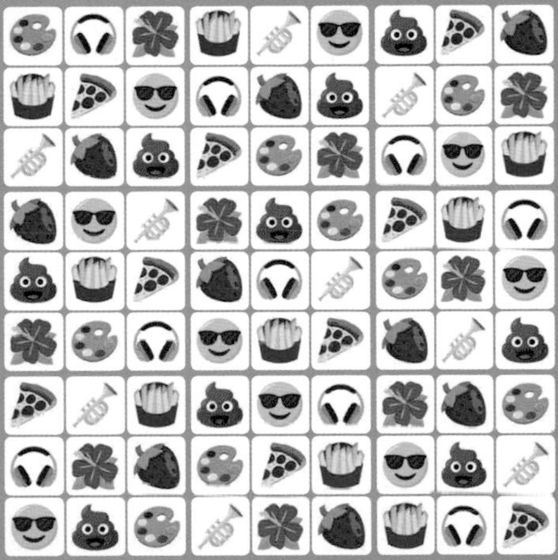

85

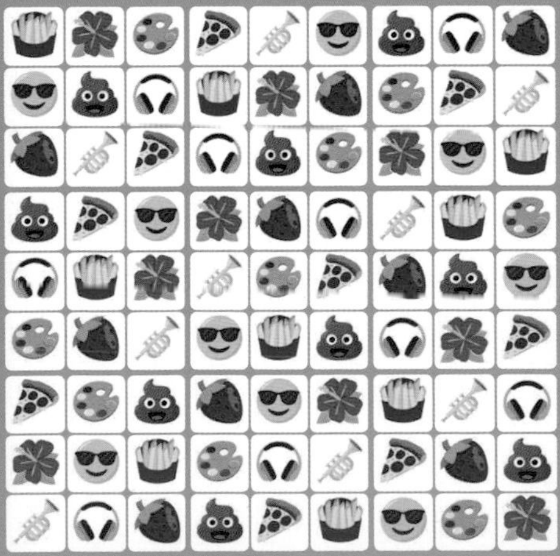

86

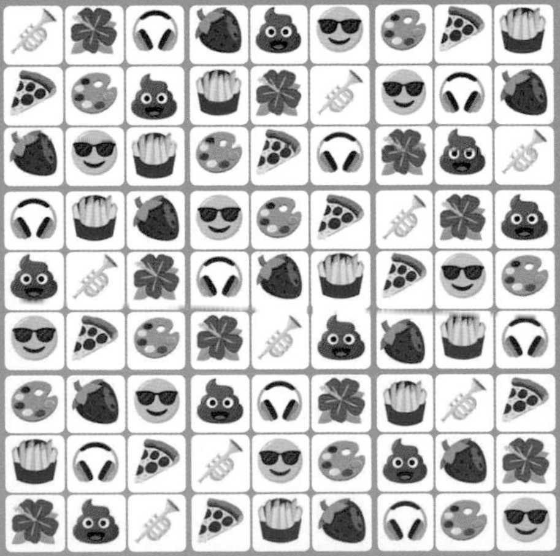

87

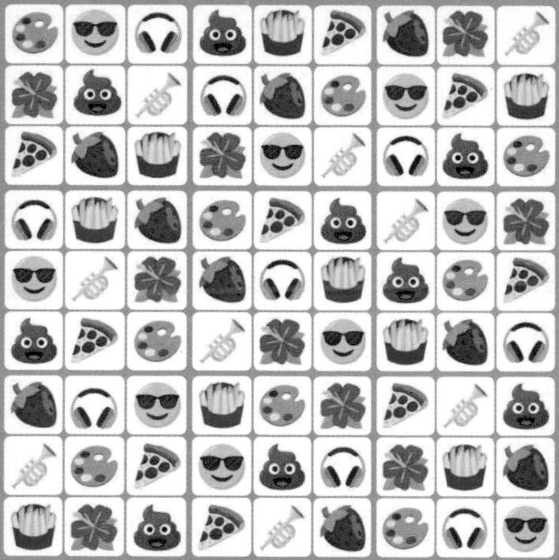

88

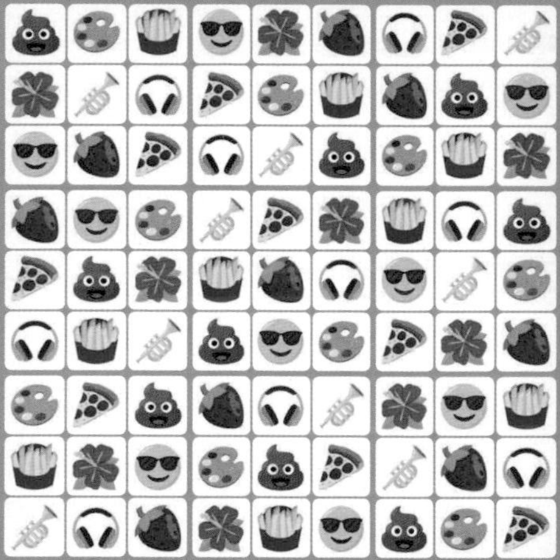

89

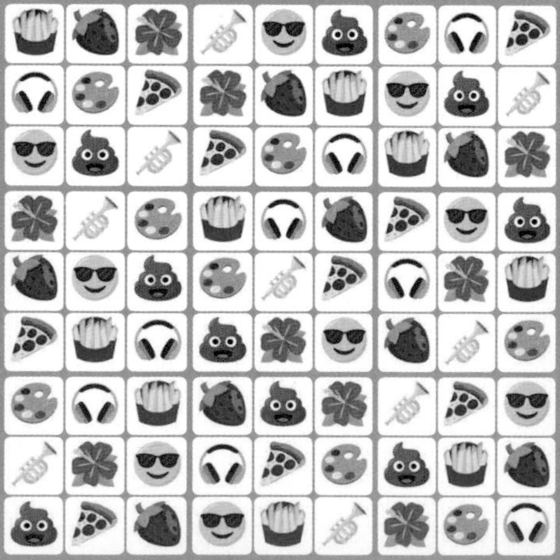

90

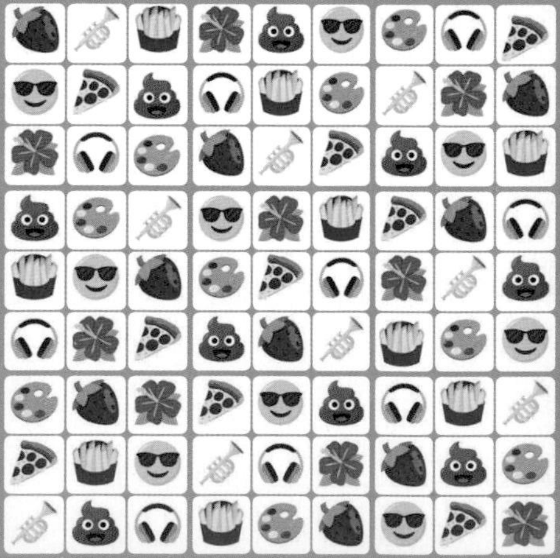

91

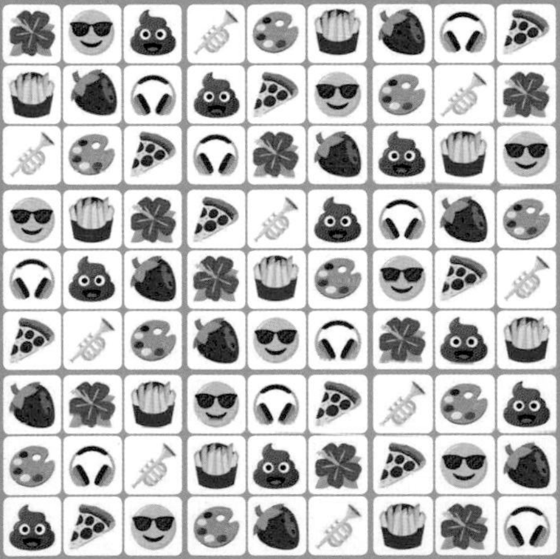

92

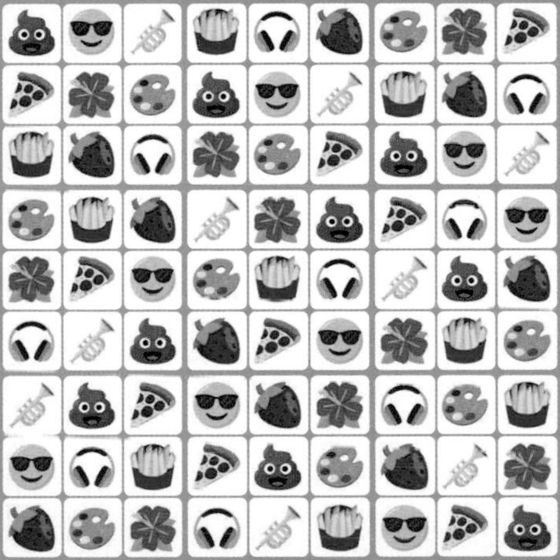

93

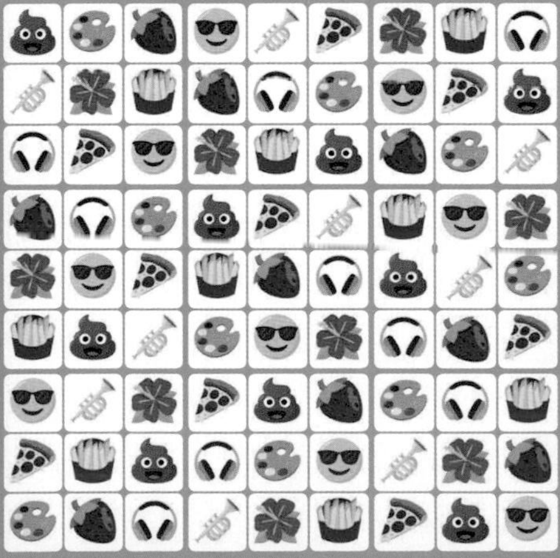

94

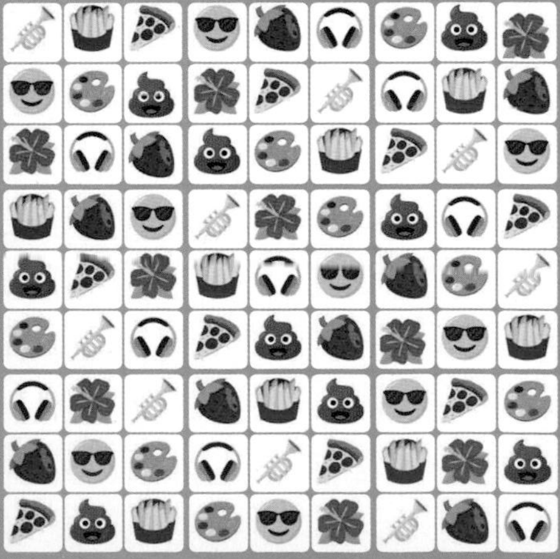

95

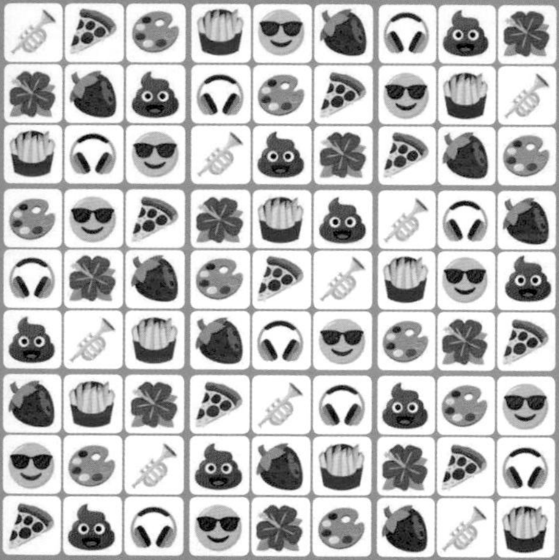

96

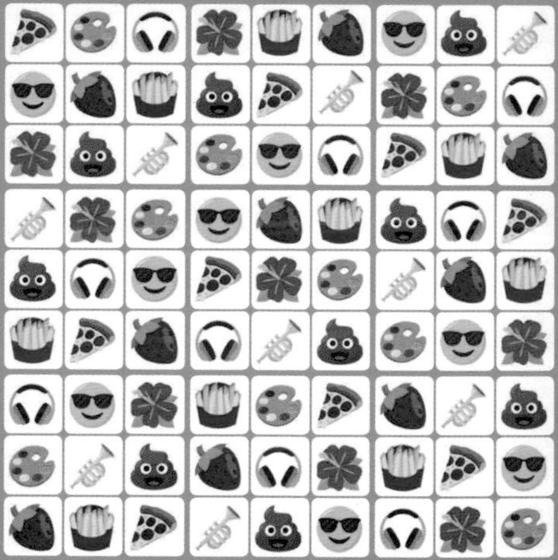

97

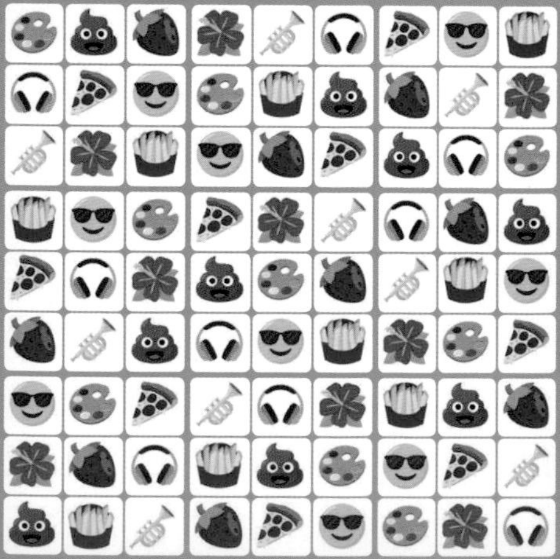

98

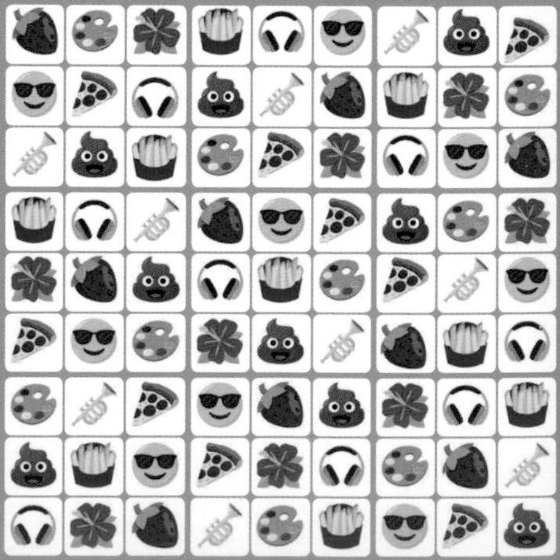

99

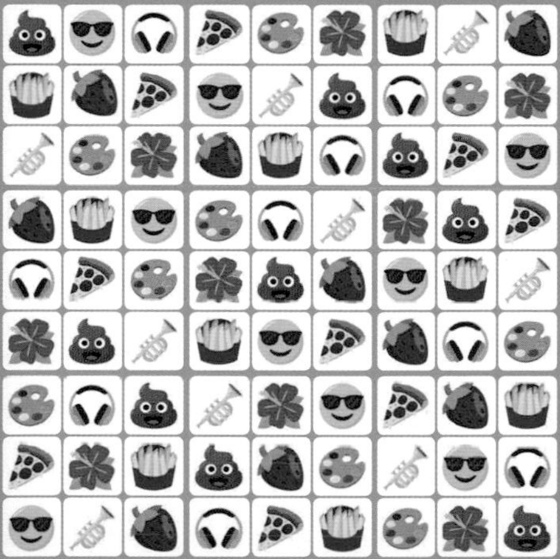

100

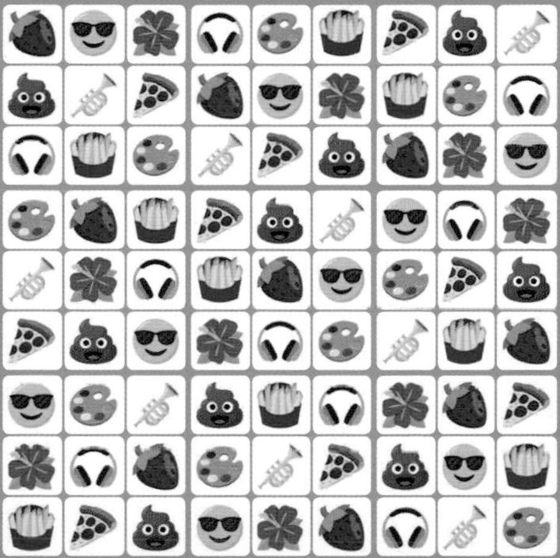

101

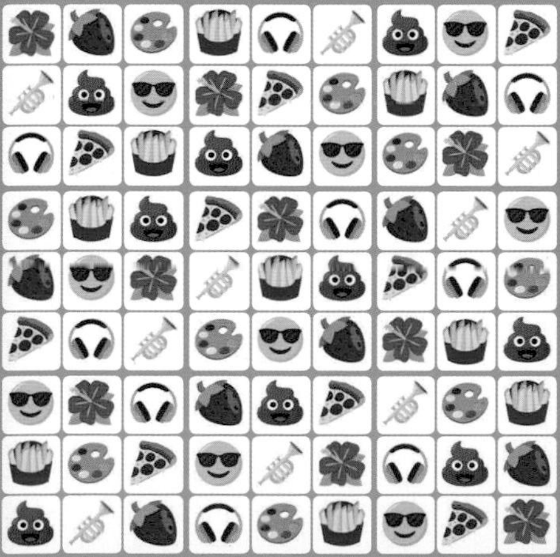

102

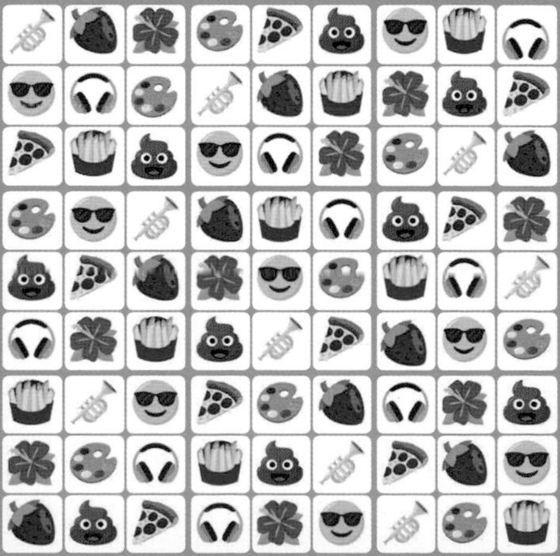

103

104

105

SOLUTIONS: HARD